report
2002:
a man's guide
to women

hot days

steamy nights

surefire seductions

scorching sex

edited by Leah Flickinger

RODALE

Sex and Values at Rodale

We believe that an active and healthy sex life, based on mutual consent and respect between partners, is an important component of physical and mental well-being. We also respect that sex is a private matter and that each person has a different opinion of what sexual practices or levels of discourse are appropriate. Rodale is committed to offering responsible, practical advice about sexual matters, supported by accredited professionals and legitimate scientific research. Our goal—for sex and all other topics—is to publish information that empowers people's lives.

Notice

This book is intended as a reference volume only, not as a medical manual. The information given here is designed to help you make informed decisions about your health. It is not intended as a substitute for any treatment that may have been prescribed by your doctor. If you suspect that you have a medical problem, we urge you to seek competent medical help.

Mention of specific companies, organizations, or authorities in this book does not imply endorsement by the publisher, nor does mention of specific companies, organizations, or authorities in the book imply that they endorse the book.

Internet addresses and telephone numbers given in this book were accurate at the time this book went to press.

RODALE

WE **INSPIRE** AND **ENABLE** PEOPLE TO IMPROVE
THEIR LIVES AND THE WORLD AROUND THEM

Report 2002: A Man's Guide to Women Staff

EDITOR: Leah Flickinger

ASSOCIATE EDITOR: Kathryn C. LeSage

WRITERS: Brett Bara; Mickie Barg; Jeffrey Bouley; Michael Castleman; Carolyn McAtee Cerbin; Shane DuBow; Jennifer Everett; Leah Flickinger; Kimberly Flynn; Linda Formichelli; Perry Garfinkel; Ron Geraci; Brian Good; Debra Gordon; Melissa Gotthardt; Steve Gourley; Joshua Green; Greg Gutfeld; Jennifer Haigh; Corey Hann; Kristin Harmel; Terrance Henderson; Keith Hopcroft; Alex James; Jennifer Johannesen; Mark Jolly; Lisa Jones; Brian Paul Kaufman; Barbara Keesling, Ph.D.; Larry Keller; Rob Kemp; Judy Kuriansky, Ph.D.; Jeffrey Lindenmuth; Joe Mackie; Christian Millman; Tanya Oakes; Hugh O'Neill; Wallace G. Pinfold; Deanna Portz; Carol Potera; Dori Rebich; Jessica Rossi; Joe Schwartz; Ted Spiker; Joel Stein; Bill Stieg; Duane Swierczynski; Andrew Taber; Zachary Veilleux; Angela Walker; Bill White; Tom Zoellner

ART DIRECTOR: Charles Beasley

SERIES DESIGNER: Tanja Lipinski Cole

INTERIOR AND COVER DESIGNER: Susan P. Eugster

RESEARCH EDITOR: Deborah Pedron

SENIOR RESEARCHER: Deanna Portz

EDITORIAL RESEARCHER: Bernadette Sukley

INTERNATIONAL EDITORIAL COORDINATOR: Charlene Lutz

LAYOUT DESIGNER: Faith Hague

PRODUCT SPECIALIST: Jodi Schaffer

contents

5 ORCHESTRATE SIZZLING DATES

6 SEX IN THE PUBLIC EYE

7 SIDESTEP THE SEX POLICE

8 SPOT-CHECK CYBERSEX

introduction

Recently, we surveyed you and your fellow readers on your favorite sources of sex information. Your top picks? Books, in a dead heat with your wife or girl-friend.

I, for one, am glad to hear that. And I have two excellent reasons why.

First, I'm in the book business, and I've spent a good portion of the past year immersing myself in up-to-the-minute sex information.

Second, I share an important characteristic with your wife or girlfriend: I'm a woman.

Yes, a woman. A woman who reads all the latest surveys on sex. A woman who scours the Internet for sex-related sites, schleps to sex conferences (a tough job, I know), and browses the popular men's mags. A woman who's clued in to exactly the kind of sex information guys say they want. And though I don't have a penis, let's just say I understand the basic concept.

Besides, who better to edit a book called *A Man's Guide to Women* than, well, a woman?

This particular woman has packed this particular edition with tons of new and different stuff on sex and relationships. What could possibly be new and different in the world of sex? Here's just a small sampling.

● Your most powerful sex fuel

It's high-test. Testosterone, that is. Learn how to maximize the natural stuff your body produces so you can give the sexual performance of your life. Every time.

● The science of sex

Think the drug companies hit the jackpot with Viagra? They've only just begun. You'll get inside information on a drug that will help increase *her* libido, from one of the guys who did the research.

● Caveman sex

I don't mean sex of the club-wielding, me-want-woman-now variety; that's a different book. Here we're talking the best actual coital cave in the United States, along with 34 other ultimate and original venues for getting it on. Suf-fice it to say that if you're like me, you'll never look at a washing machine the same way again.

● The disposable man
Tired of being The Protector, Mr. Fix-It, Everything-to-Everyone? You're not alone. Learn how feminism has shortchanged you, from Warren Farrell, a former feminist who's now a men's advocate.

● The key to more sex
It's respect. Sock it to her, and the sex will get better and better. Trust me on this one.

● 12 weird penis tricks
We'll explain the mysteries of every member.

● A stripper's life
Why it pays to be nice to women who take their clothes off, from Julia Query, professional dancer and director of the documentary *Live Nude Girls Unite!*

● Cybersex 101
Yeah, I know: If they'd had courses like this when you were in college, you would have made Dean's List all 4 years. Read Professor Mary Madden's definition of cybersex. It's an even wilder world than you think.

So allow me to guide you through the complex maze of sex and sexuality. Think of me as your wife or girlfriend—or both, if you like. In fact, why not think of me as *all* your preferred sources of sex information rolled into one?
You'll be glad you did.
Happy reading,

—Leah Flickinger
Editor

1

TUNE UP YOUR SEX MACHINE

 Musicians are wise people. Take violinists, for example. They know that if you want to give your best performance, you have to take good care of your instrument. If it's cracked or out-of-tune, it won't make pretty music. And, they tell us, a well-cared-for violin sounds richer and stronger the older it gets.

We know that, unlike a Stradivarius, your penis doesn't always play better with age (and it won't fetch six figures at auction). Of course, that doesn't mean your sex life is doomed to collect dust. With a little effort, all your working parts can keep making music—playing duets, if you catch our drift—right up to the last crescendo.

The best news of all? All the violinists we know say that you absolutely, positively must fiddle regularly to keep your violin primed. Read on to learn how to keep your favorite instrument ready to play at any time.

TOP TEN

Sex Injuries
and How to Treat Them

Sex injuries are our favorite kind of injuries—unless they're self-inflicted, of course. Here's how to treat common bumps and bruises that can happen during a good night's work.

① **Rug burn.** If you've skinned your elbows or knees, rub the wounds with an antibiotic ointment like Polysporin. Then cover them with nonstick bandages so they'll stay moist until they scab over. Next time, throw a soft cotton blanket on the floor.

② **Penile fracture.** When a fracture occurs, you'll hear a loud snap or pop, accompanied by swelling, bruising, excruciating pain, and the expletive of your choice. Put ice (wrapped in a towel) on your penis and have her drive you to an ER. "Penile fractures can be fixed surgically, but the longer you wait, the worse your prognosis," says James B. Regan, M.D., a urologist at Georgetown University's medical center in Washington, D.C.

③ **Bite wound.** A human bite is even worse than an animal bite, because the average mouth carries so many different kinds of bacteria. Wash the wound thoroughly and look for redness, swelling, or discharge. If you notice these signs of infection or have a fever, see a doctor.

④ **Fingernail marks.** As long as your skin's not broken, moisturizer should make the scratches go away in a day or so. If she clawed you until you bled, you need to apply Polysporin—and you're doing something right.

⑤ **Sore penis.** Congratulations! Treat it like any other abrasion—use moisturizer (one that's made for sensitive skin) to help speed up healing. Try not to get carried away with this treatment.

⑥ **Suction marks.** Excessive suction can cause small blood vessels under the skin to break, spilling blood into the surrounding tissue and turning the area red (the young folk call it a hickey). It'll change from red to blue to brown to yellow before it heals in a couple of weeks. Topical vitamin K might help it heal faster. Look for a cream containing phytonadione, and a turtleneck.

7 **Sunburn.** Beach blanket bingo is your thing? Put out the fire with over-the-counter anti-inflammatories such as aspirin or ibuprofen. Taking them as soon as possible after a sunburn will minimize tissue damage, says Vail Reese, M.D., a dermatologist with the Dermatology Medical Group of San Francisco. Take them as directed on the package label for 2 days after the burn. Sit in a cool (not cold) bath or an Aveeno oatmeal bath for further relief.

If you have blistering, severe pain, or, um, excessive swelling, see your doc. He may take pity on you and prescribe oral cortisone. Next time, take cover under a beach umbrella.

8 **Leg cramp.** Your leg muscles—the power behind all those thrusts—are the most likely muscles to cramp during sex. You're probably not well hydrated, says Lewis G. Maharam, M.D., a New York sports-medicine specialist. Stretch out the muscle until it stops cramping. To prevent future cramps, drink one or two glasses of water during that precoital dinner.

9 **Rash.** Redness or a rash on your penis could be a symptom of any number of things, including a sexually transmitted disease. If you've ruled that out with a trip to your doc, it could be a latex allergy. Try using a polyurethane condom such as Durex Avanti instead. Still get red blotches after sex? You could be allergic to *her*. "Allergens like pollen, mold, dust, and pet dander can enter a person's system and make their way into her secretions," says Steven Witkin, Ph.D., an immunologist at Cornell University medical center in Ithaca, New York. Washing up right after sex and using a condom both help. So does taking an over-the-counter antihistamine (like Benadryl) an hour or so before sex.

10 **Injured testicle.** Take a stray knee between the legs, and chances are the pain and nausea will last only a few minutes. If it's worse than that, lie on your back and place a rolled-up hand towel under your scrotum to keep the blood from pooling. Then put ice (wrapped in a towel) on it for 5 to 10 minutes. If there's swelling or discoloration, see a doctor to make sure you haven't fractured a testicle. And stop dating Rockettes.

MUST READS

Penis Peculiarities

You probably regard your penis the same way the old lady next door regards her cat: You think it's unique, extraordinary, blessed with strange and quirky attributes not seen elsewhere on the planet.

Wrong. In both cases, there are billions of clones that do the same tricks and cough up the same hairballs. Here, Zachary Veilleux lays out a dozen odd moves every member makes.

● It keeps whizzing after you've zipped up.

Notice how gasoline hoses always spill a few drops after you've flipped the pump off? Your hose has a similar design. The sphincter muscle that pinches the urethra closed is about 8 inches from the tip of your penis, so some urine is always trapped in front of it, says Irving J. Fishman, M.D., a urologist at the Baylor school of medicine in Houston, Texas. A press behind your scrotum can help you avoid dotting your trousers, or you can use a technique called urethral milking. Simply run your finger along the underside of your penis to force out remaining liquid, says Dr. Fishman. One study, reported in the *British Journal of Urology*, found that this little trick reduced postpee dribble by nearly 30 percent. It's scary that somebody actually had to measure this.

● It ejaculates when you bench-press.

When you contract your pelvic muscles, they exert pressure on the prostate and seminal vesicles and can squeeze out some seminal fluid. The easiest way to stop staining your gym shorts? "Ejaculate more often," says Laurence A. Levine, M.D., professor of urology at Rush-Presbyterian–St. Luke's Medical Center in Chicago.

● It has a twist.

Like a cheap plastic toy, your body is made from two halves welded together. (For proof, check the seam inside your mouth and under your scrotum.) The two sides develop at slightly different rates before you're born, and that leaves one telltale sign: a slight twist in your penis. "It's called penile torsion, and almost all men have it to a slight degree," says James Cummings, M.D., chief of urology at the University of Southern Alabama. It's harmless unless your penis twists more than 90 degrees (or a quarter of the way around when it's flaccid). See a urologist in that case; it could cause erection problems down the road. A handy icebreaker: Penises always twist counterclockwise, and no one knows why.

◉ It leaks during foreplay.

When you're aroused, your Cowper's glands, located at the base of your penis (bet you didn't know you had them), produce a liquid that lubricates and deacidifies your urethra so semen can blast through unfettered—sort of like a soldier swathing a cannon before firing. The longer you stay erect, the more of this "preejaculate" you make. And it can contain sperm, which is one reason pulling out fails as a birth-control measure.

◉ It won't urinate publicly.

One in 10 men has a disorder called paruresis, which is a fancy name for stage fright. When you're nervous (maybe your boss is grumbling at the next urinal), the muscles that control urination involuntarily tighten, capping your flow. "Some men with severe cases of paruresis can't urinate in a public restroom unless there's no one else there," says Joseph Himle, Ph.D., a psychologist at the University of Michigan. The best solution: Find a stall and lock the door. That'll give you enough privacy to relax and start things flowing (reading a paper helps). If there's no stall handy, take a deep breath and contract your pelvic muscles, then relax and exhale. Repeat until you hear a trickle.

◉ You aim straight, it pees left.

Why does your urine stream sometimes takes a left turn into the bathtub? The problem is your meatus, or the tiny opening at the tip of your penis. "Urine spirals out of your urethra like a bullet out of a gun," says Dr. Levine. "If there's dried mucus, ejaculate, or any other irregularity in the meatus, it can make the stream split or go off-center." This happens most often in the morning or after sex. To avoid wetting the bathroom floor, gently part your meatus with your fingers before urinating. Or step up and aim for the tub. If this happens often,

SEX TRENDS

THE HARD TRUTH

Surveys of penis size are like asking Geraldo how important he is: You expect some exaggeration. Erection pollsters typically have trusted guys to measure themselves and tell the truth. *As if.* Recently, the condom maker LifeStyles set up a tent in Cancun during spring break, invited 401 college guys, provided girlie mags, and had two nurses measure (with a doctor supervising). The average length of an erect penis was 5.877 inches. That's a quarter-inch to a half-inch shorter than in previous surveys. Average girth (crucial for condom making): 4.972 inches. Our favorite stat: Twenty-five percent could not rise to the occasion.

> **"** Most men simply don't look at enough genitals to know what's normal. **"**
>
> —James Cummings, M.D., chief of urology at the University of South Alabama

see a urologist. There may be a problem in your urethra.

● **It may be pink, purple, or blue.**
"The skin on the head of your penis is thinner than the shaft skin, so it changes color easily in response to bloodflow," says Dr. Levine. It's normal to sport a red knob when you're aroused and a purple one when you're not. However, bright red—especially if it's accompanied by itching, pain, discharge, or lesions—is a symptom of infection or an allergic reaction (possibly to latex). Black means your bloodflow has been cut off; go to a hospital.

● **It shrinks when wet.**
This skinny-dipping horror occurs because penile muscles contract when they're cold, says Dr. Levine. A gentle tug can help loosen these muscles and restore some of your normal length. But do this discreetly, or she'll think you prefer swimming alone.

● **It gets hard for no reason.**
You're on the bus, sitting across from a chatty redhead. Suddenly you're using a magazine to hide an erection. "Unwanted erections often occur when you become sexually aroused subconsciously," says Dr. Cummings. For instance, the woman might be wearing the same perfume as your college girlfriend, and your brain picked up this long-dormant cue. Vibrations can also spur erections, which is why school-bus stiffies were so common. Your only game plan? "Seek cover and wait," says Dr. Cummings. Never force an erection down; that can cause penile fractures. Sadly, the inadvertent woody fades with time: Surprise erections become rare after age 30.

● **It curves like a banana when erect.**
That's normal. Actually, a straight penis is quite rare. If you have the typical curve of 30 degrees or less (like a banana), it shouldn't cause you trouble. But if your curve is more severe or if intercourse hurts, you're among the 2 percent of men who have Peyronie's disease. It's caused by tiny patches of scar tissue brought about by erection-bending mishaps, such as missed thrusts, unlucky rollovers in bed, and erections stuffed into jeans. One traumatic injury—even to a flaccid penis (remember the soccer penalty kick?)—can cause it. This scar tissue doesn't expand, and that causes your erection to curve. A urologist can prescribe drugs or surgery to straighten you out, says Dr. Levine.

❍ It gets stuck during sex.

No it doesn't. We know, you've heard about couples becoming clamped at the crotch; in 1980, the *British Medical Journal* even published a London doctor's 1947 recollection of penis captivus in which a couple was brought into the ER on one stretcher. But this intriguing phenomenon has never really been proved to occur, says Dr. Cummings. If your partner's vaginal muscles begin to spasm violently during intercourse (a condition called vaginismus), it'll cause her pain and make you feel mild tightness, but considering the vaginal anatomy, "it just isn't possible to get your penis trapped in there," says Dr. Cummings.

❍ It turns to stone.

One in 40,000 of you will suffer priapism, a persistent, painful erection that lasts longer than 2 hours and doesn't subside when that redhead sashays out of sight. Usually caused by a blockage in the penis, or by needlessly taking a drug like Viagra, priapism isn't something to mess around with. Rush to an emergency room if it happens, as the condition can cause tissue damage and impotence. And be careful with rubber bands. That's all we're saying.

Tap Your Testosterone

Forget beer. The fluid that makes a man tick doesn't come from a bottle or a keg—it comes from you. Yep, it's testosterone, and it's far more potent than anything made of hops. The average guy (that would be you) has about 1.5 milligrams of the stuff in his bloodstream at any given time. It regulates your sex drive, triggers your erections, and gives you the confidence to approach unapproachable women. Every guy has testosterone, but some have a little more than others. They're the ones with thick, rippled muscles and the kind of sex lives HBO makes documentaries about. Want to be that guy? Ron Geraci tells you how.

Testosterone helps you build muscle, burn belly fat, maintain strong bones, achieve rock-hard erections, grow a decent beard, and demand another 10 grand from your boss—or else. "Having adequate testosterone is critical for maintaining lean muscle mass, sexual potency, and cognitive function," says Adrian Dobs, M.D., an endocrinologist at Johns Hopkins University in Baltimore. Without it, you'd be an androgynous cartoon character. A slow-moving schnook. A guy on Hollywood Squares.

Examples abound. "Between 4 million and 5 million men have low testosterone levels right now, and 95 percent of them don't know it," says Ken Goldberg, M.D., a urologist and director of the Male Health Center in Dallas.

The normal level of testosterone in your bloodstream is between 350 and 1,000 nanograms per deciliter (ng/dl). Like combable hair, those quantities silently start to wane around age 40. You lose about 1 percent a year—a harmless decline in the short term, but a cause of obesity, brittle bones, muscle loss, and impotence by the time you reach your 60s—if you live that long. Testosterone levels in the low range (a blood serum score below 350 ng/dl) may increase your chances of dying of a heart attack.

perfect figures

NOW, IF YOU COULD ONLY CONVINCE HER IT TASTES GOOD.

Number of calories per ejaculation: 5 to 25

. . . .

It's not just an old man's problem, either. Men in their 30s and 40s also fall prey to low testosterone counts. It's a disorder called hypogonadism, and it can be caused by an undescended testicle, a testicular injury, a pituitary-gland disorder, or even some prescription drugs. It usually goes undiagnosed until a man hits his doctor with a tell-tale complaint: "I can't get an erection."

"If you have reduced levels of sexual desire, have your testosterone level checked immediately," says Allen Seftel, M.D., a urologist at Case Western Reserve University Hospitals of Cleveland. You can replenish your testosterone stores with injections, gels, pills, or patches, but these medical treatments are no panacea: Side effects include acne, high cholesterol, shrunken testicles, and liver damage. Further, don't take supplements like DHEA or androstenedione to boost testosterone; they might increase your risks of prostate cancer and heart disease.

"For men with borderline testosterone scores, I advise them to try to raise their levels through exercise and weight loss before going on testosterone therapy," says Dr. Goldberg. And it might pay to start young. "Since your testosterone declines at a steady rate, it's conceivable that raising your hormone levels naturally in your 20s and 30s could help you maintain higher levels later on," he says. Either way, the reward can be a stronger physique—and better bedroom sessions—than you'd otherwise deserve. Below are 13 tips designed to get your juice up safely.

● **Get rid of the flopping belly...**

If you don't, you may grow a pair of fetching breasts to complement it. Carrying excess body fat elevates your estrogen levels, and that may cause your testosterone levels to sink, says Joseph Zmuda, Ph.D., an epidemiologist at the University of Pittsburgh. Two or three extra pounds won't cause this hormonal shift; it only occurs if you're 30 percent over your ideal body weight. "Unfortunately, that's pretty common now," says Dr. Dobs.

● **...but lose only 1 pound a week.**

When you want to trim down quickly, you probably starve yourself while exercising like a madman. One of the many reasons this stops working in your 30s, when your natural testosterone levels start dropping, is pretty simple: Cutting your calorie intake by more than 15 percent makes your brain think you're starving, so it shuts down testosterone production to wait out the famine. "There's no need to reproduce if you're starving," explains Thomas Incledon, C.S.C.S., R.D., of Human Performance Specialists in Plantation, Florida. Ironically, this dive in circulating testosterone stops you from burning body fat efficiently, so you're actually thwarting your hard efforts to melt that tire off your gut.

● **Skip the Atkins fad.**

Research suggests that eating a high-protein, low-carbohydrate diet can cramp your testosterone levels. High amounts of dietary protein in your blood can eventually lower the amount of testosterone produced in your testes, says

The Highs and Lows of Testosterone

In step with your circadian rhythm, your testosterone levels spike and plummet throughout the day. They peak in the morning (to help you get out of bed and kill breakfast) and then drop by as much as 20 percent by bedtime. Your lifetime testosterone levels follow a more predictable trajectory: The incredible surge in your 30s naturally gives way to a long, steep decline. This may mysteriously affect your attitudes toward combat and minivans.

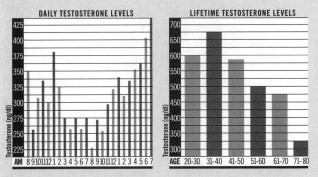

SOURCE: STEPHEN J. WINTERS, M.D., UNIVERSITY OF LOUISVILLE

Incledon, who observed this relationship in a Pennsylvania State University study of 12 healthy, athletic men.

Your protein intake should be about 16 percent of your daily calories, Incledon says. So, if you're an average 170-pound man who eats 2,900 calories a day, you should eat about 140 grams of protein daily, which is about the amount in two chicken breasts and a 6-ounce can of tuna.

● Have morning sex.

German scientists found that simply having an erection causes your circulating testosterone to rise significantly—and having one in the morning can goose your natural postdawn testosterone surge. It's a sure bet you'll burn a little fat, too.

● Stick with tough exercises.

To beef up your testosterone levels, the bulk of your workout should involve "compound" weight-lifting exercises that train several large muscle groups, and not just one or two smaller muscles. For example, studies have shown that doing squats, bench presses, or back rows increases testosterone more than doing biceps curls or triceps pushdowns, even though the effort may seem the same. This is why doing squats could help you build bigger biceps.

● Make nuts your midnight snack.

Nuts are good for your nuts. Research has found that men who eat diets rich in monounsaturated fat—the kind found in peanuts—have the highest testosterone levels. "It's not known why this occurs, but some scientists believe that monounsaturated fats have a direct effect on the testes," says Incledon. Nuts, olive oil, canola oil, and peanut

SEX TRENDS

TESTOSTERONE IN A TUBE

If your testosterone levels dip so low that your doc advises supplementation, Androgel, the first replacement gel to get FDA approval, should make life easier. "It's not that other testosterone preparations don't work," says Ronald Swerdloff, M.D., a professor at Harbor-UCLA Medical Center, "but Androgel is very convenient." Rub it on your shoulders or stomach, and the skin serves as a reservoir, slowly and steadily releasing the hormone into your system all day. Studies show that Androgel prevents the testosterone peaks and valleys that shots and pills can cause. It also increases a few of our favorite things, including sex drive, bone density, and lean muscle mass.

butter are good sources of mo-nounsaturated fat.

● **Squeeze out five repetitions per set.**
Throwing around 5-pound dumbbells won't help you effect a rise in testosterone. Start off by using a heavy weight that you can lift only five times. That weight is about 85 percent of your one-repetition maximum. A Finnish study found that this workload produced the greatest boosts in testosterone.

● **Do three sets of each weight-lifting movement.**
Researchers at Pennsylvania State University determined that this fosters greater increases in testosterone than just one or two sets. Rest a full minute between sets, so you can regain enough strength to continue lifting at least 70 percent of your one-rep maximum during the second and third sets.

● **Rest harder than you work out.**
If you overtrain—meaning you

Running on Fumes?

If you've experienced any of the symptoms below for more than a few weeks, your testosterone levels may be below the 350 ng/dl mark. Immediately stop watching *Friends* and ask your doctor to give you a serum-testosterone blood test (this should be done in the morning). If your score is indeed low, get retested, and also request a blood-prolactin test to rule out pituitary-gland cancer, says Martin Resnick, M.D., a urologist at Case Western Reserve University in Cleveland.

SYMPTOMS OF LOW TESTOSTERONE

● You couldn't care less about having sex.

● You've been having erection problems.

● You're depressed and lethargic for no good reason.

● You seem to have lost muscle mass in your upper body, even though you lift weights.

● You're over 55 years old.

● You're losing body hair.

● Your breasts are growing.

don't allow your body to recuperate adequately between training sessions—your circulating testosterone levels can plunge by as much as 40 percent, according to a study at the University of North Carolina. The symptoms of overtraining are hard to miss: irritability, insomnia, muscle shrinkage, joining the Reform party. To avoid overtraining, make sure you sleep a full 8 hours at night, and never stress the same muscles with weight-lifting movements 2 days in a row.

● Drive home sober.
To maintain a healthy testosterone count—and titanium erections—cut yourself off after a maximum of three drinks. "Binge drinking will kill your testosterone levels," warns Incledon. Alcohol affects the endocrine system, causing your testes to stop producing the male hormone. That's one reason drinking often causes you to go limp at the moment of truth—or to start blubbering about your ex.

● Have a sandwich at 3:00 P.M.
As any sensible woman knows, the way to put hair on a man's chest is to fill his stomach. Your body needs a ready supply of calories to make testosterone, so regularly skipping meals or going for long stretches without eating can cause your hormone levels to plummet. Then again, that's probably the warden's plan.

● Convince her to buy the fried tortilla chips.
If you want to raise your testosterone score, eat a diet composed of about 30 percent fat, and not much less. Your body needs dietary fat to produce testosterone, so eating like a vegetarian aerobics instructor will cause your testosterone levels to sink drastically. This is bad—unless you actually *are* a vegetarian aerobics instructor.

● Stop surfing for porn at 2:00 A.M.
Sleeping less than 7 to 8 hours a night can screw up your circadian rhythm. That's why your testosterone levels are higher in the morning after a good night's sleep. So if your work or social schedule keeps you stooped in perpetual jet lag, don't be surprised if you stop craving sex. At least that'll make it easier to stay out of bed.

Make a Good Erection Even Better

You don't give up on a good, functional, reliable vehicle just because it's got a few extra miles on it, even if it doesn't have just-off-the-lot acceleration or perfect alignment. It takes you where you need to go. Still, there's not a guy around who doesn't dream of arriving in style—and impressing all the girls.

Wait, are we still talking about cars?

Of course not. So we'll skip the rest of the jokes about fully-inflated tires and fuel injectors and cut to the chase: Even if your erections are nothing to complain about, they could probably be better. Brian Good outlines 16 ways to have the hardest, best erections of your life:

◐ Tie one on.

There's a reason constriction rings are one of the old standbys for enhancing erections. "Constriction rings help trap blood to make your penis hard, and keeps it from flowing back into your body," says Greta Christina, the general manager of www.blowfish.com, an online sex-toy retailer. "It can't give you an erection if you don't already have one, but it can make your erection harder and help keep you hard." The secret to getting the most from the ring? Put it at the very base of the penis—behind your testicles—rather than on the shaft. That will help it stay on better. "Beginners should start off with a buckling or snapping ring instead of a solid one, because there's less of a chance of the ring getting stuck," says Christina. ER doctors have enough to worry about without having to remove your stuck constriction ring. (Men with circulatory or neurological problems like diabetes shouldn't use constriction rings without a doctor's okay.)

> **" If you don't want cancer, feel your balls. "**
>
> —comedian Tom Green, after his testicular-cancer diagnosis

◐ Have sex in the morning.

Not only do you get the benefit of a natural morning erection (caused by your bladder putting pressure on your prostate), you also have more energy for the act itself. "After a busy day at work, you can't expect your body to have enough energy for a long bout of sex," says Felice Dunas, author of *Passion Play*. Instead of trying to make love when you're tired, spend the night cuddling with your partner, and set the alarm a half-hour early. "Your erections will be stronger in the morning because you'll feel more energized, and the extra night of contact with your partner will make you even more aroused in the morning," says Dunas.

◐ Work out.

"It doesn't matter what you do, or even how well you do it," says Hank C. K. Wuh, M.D., author of *Sexual Fitness*. "What's important is that you find something physical you enjoy doing—jogging, walking, gardening, lifting weights—and that you do it regularly, at least three times a week." The benefit: Exercise increases your testosterone production and reduces cholesterol levels. "Men with high cholesterol levels have twice the risk of erection problems, so even moderately elevated cholesterol levels can have an impact on erections," says Dr. Wuh. "Exercise also improves blood flow through your body, and the better your circulation, the firmer your erections will be."

❍ Have *her* for dessert . . .

. . . instead of the chocolate cake. Your erection will appreciate it, since blood flow to your penis is at its strongest when you're in an upright, sitting position, according to Drogo K. Montague, M.D., director of the Center for Sexual Function at the Cleveland Clinic Foundation. Look for a sturdy upholstered chair, without arms if possible. Have your partner straddle you, with her feet pressed flat against the seat of the chair. As things heat up, she can control both the pacing and depth of penetration by raising and lowering herself.

❍ Play with her toys.

"Most men think of vibrators as women's toys, but they can also be fun for men," says Carol Queen, Ed.D., director of continuing education and staff sexologist at Good Vibrations (www.goodvibes.com). Her suggestion: try having your partner rub her vibrator along the head of your penis during foreplay. "Some men won't enjoy the feeling, but it will drive some men crazy," she says. If you're one of the guys who enjoys it, there are also pouches and constrictor rings with built-in vibrators. "Most of these products combine constriction with vibration, giving guys the best of both worlds," says Queen.

❍ Skip the romantic meal.

"Don't do the wining and dining thing if you also want a really hard erection," says Dunas. When you eat a big meal or drink alcohol, your body needs extra blood to digest the food or remove the alcohol from your system. "If that blood is being sent to your stomach, it leaves less blood to go to your penis and you end up with a weaker erection," she says.

❍ Learn to like it rough.

Want to try something new? Here's Queen's suggestion for a type of stimulation most guys have never experienced: "Have your partner run her finger nails, or anything else that's slightly scratchy—like a hair brush—over the head of

Sex technique to avoid back pain: Have your partner lie back so her butt is at the foot of a low bed or couch (futons or beanbag chairs work great). Her feet should be flat on the floor. Kneel between her legs, penetrate, and lean forward. Plant your elbows on the bed to take the weight off your back, and thrust with your leg muscles (not just your hips) says Lewis G. Maharam, M.D., author of A Healthy Back.

your penis. This kind of stimulation is very exotic and unusual for most guys, and it will cause a rush of blood to the surface of the penis," she says.

● Trim that gut.

In a study of almost 2,000 men between the ages of 51 and 88, researchers found that those with a waistline measuring 42 inches or more were nearly twice as likely to suffer erectile dysfunction as men with a 32-inch waist. Even being just a few pounds overweight can impair the quality of your erections. The reason: Extra pounds impair your circulation, making it harder for blood to find its way to your penis.

● Get pumped up.

There are a number of different penis pumps on the market. "When you use a pump, all you basically do is suck additional blood into your penis, which can help to temporarily make your erection firmer," says Queen. But you need to work quickly. As soon as the pump comes off, blood starts returning to the rest of your body.

● Use your thighs.

Try pressing your thighs together as tightly as possible during sex in order to add firmness to an erection, suggests Queen. This may help tighten your PC muscles—the muscles that contract during orgasm—and it may affect blood flow to the penis as well. "Try lying on your back, putting your legs together, and letting your partner straddle you," says Queen. "Or have your partner lie on her back, with her legs apart, and then enter her with your legs pushed tightly together."

● Take turns.

"No matter how turned-on a guy is, he can always be turned on even more," says Dunas. Try alternating activities. "Do something that brings you to the brink of orgasm, then stop and move to her. When she's close, stop and get back to what she was doing to you." Your erection will get more and more firm after each break.

● Stretch out.

"Many men grab their testicles while they masturbate," says Queen. "That's because your testicles elevate and get closer to your body right before climax." By having your partner gently tug them and keep things in place for you, you'll get extra stimulation. Besides feeling great to many men, pulling down on the testicles may give a little extra staying power.

● Try a supplement.

"There are a lot of supplements that claim to enhance erections, but studies have shown one in particular to be effective," says Dr. Wuh. Several of the active ingredients in ArginMax, including the amino acid l-arginine, increase production of a molecule that relaxes muscle tissue in artery walls, improving blood flow. "In clinical research, ArginMax has been found to significantly enhance sexual fitness in men," says Dr. Wuh. At the end of a 4-week trial, 89 percent of men with mild to moderate erection problems reported improvement in the ability to maintain an erection during intercourse. You don't have to suffer from erectile dysfunction in order to benefit from taking ArginMax, however. Look for it at www.arginmax.com.

● **Exercise your penile muscles.**
We've mentioned this before, but it's worth repeating. Doing Kegel exercises can make your erections firmer, and make you last longer, too. To find the penile muscles, stop urinating midstream next time you're in the bathroom. Then, periodically flex or squeeze that same group of muscles. A couple sets of quick flicks along with several longer, 10-second squeezes each day will be enough to create a noticeable improvement in your erections.

SEX TRENDS

VIAGRA ALTERNATIVE

Looks like Viagra's got some stiff competition: the new drug Uprima. It builds an erection by triggering arousal in the brain and may help men who have had no luck with Viagra, which works by dilating blood vessels in the penis. Uprima may also be great for impatient men—not that we know any. "Uprima's biggest asset is that it's quick," says John Mulhall, M.D., director of the Center for Male Sexual Health at Loyola University in Chicago. "It takes only 15 to 20 minutes to produce an erection." Viagra takes closer to an hour. By then, we're already driving home.

● **Take the stand.**
Actors do it all the time in the movies, but when was the last time you stood during sex? Not only does it add a bit of variety to your lovemaking; it can also make your erection firmer. "We routinely ask our impotent patients to stand while we're treating them," says Wayne Hellstrom, M.D., associate professor of urology at Tulane University in New Orleans. "That's because gravity improves blood flow to the penis, ensuring a firmer erection." If you can't support your partner's weight, have her stand on a footstool and lean against a wall.

● **Switch medications.**
Although drugs like Viagra and Vardenafil can improve the strength of

your erections, certain prescription drugs might also impair that ability, and impair your sex drive as well. "Blood pressure medication, antidepressants, and even some types of cold and allergy medicines can have an effect on the quality of your erection," says Dr. Wuh. "Don't stop taking a prescription, but if you think one of your regular medications could be having an effect on the quality of your sex life, discuss the problem with your doctor," he says.

THE FUNNY PAGE

"Now, that's product placement!"

HELP ONLINE

WHAT THE HECK IS JELQUING?

Read this monthly newsletter to find out. It's produced by Men's Health
Institute, the same guys that bring you *Men's Health* magazine.
This site is loaded with advice on heating up your sex life:
Ways for you to last longer. How to find her hidden hotspot. Tips for
the best self-pleasure ever. There's even a chat room and web forum
where you can post questions and swap advice with other guys.
www.sexandhealth.com

PROTECT YOUR PROSTATE

Prostate cancer strikes more men than any another type of cancer.
When caught early, it has a good chance of being cured. That's why
this site, run by the Prostate Cancer Research Institute, is so vital to guys
who've been diagnosed with the disease. The Institute is dedicated
to educating the public, as well as to raising money for research
and finding new ways to prevent and treat prostate cancer. Look up
an unfamiliar medical term, learn about clinical trials, ask a doc
your pressing question, make a donation to the Institute's cause,
or read about ways you can help your own treatment.
www.prostate-cancer.org

DARE TO COMPARE

Want to know how you measure up? Stop stealing glances at the guy
at the next urinal and check out nobscan.com. The site posts scanned
pictures of flaccid, male genitalia. Since nothing is shown standing tall,
it's not considered porn. Still, you'd better wait for the boss
to exit your station before logging on.
www.nobscan.com

MAN'S GUIDE INTERVIEW

Wellbutrin-SR:
The Next Sex Wonderdrug?

An Interview with Drug Researcher Jack Modell, M.D.

While many antidepressants relieve depression, they sometimes replace it with another problem: a plummeting libido. The paradoxical result? A sex life even worse than before the depression started. Depressing, huh?

Get ready for some good news. Researchers have found at least one antidepressant, a relative underdog called Wellbutrin-SR [bupropion hydrochloride], that may not only avoid disrupting sex drive but may even enhance it. We talked with antidepressant researcher Jack Modell, M.D., a psychopharmacologist and a professor of psychiatry at the University of Alabama at Birmingham.

MAN'S GUIDE: **Tell us about your studies on Wellbutrin-SR.**

DR. MODELL: Several years ago—in the late 1980s—I noticed some things with regard to the sex drives of my patients who were taking antidepressants that are SSRIs (selective serotonin-reuptake inhibitors). Something like half of the patients in my practice who were on SSRI drugs—like Prozac [fluoxetine], Paxil [paroxetine], Luvox [fluvoxamine], and Zoloft [sertraline]—had decreased arousal, decreased orgasmic intensity, or other unfortunate sexual side effects.

Some drug companies were initially putting out figures that said these side effects occurred in a small percentage of people—yet I was seeing far higher percentages among my patients. And the funny thing is that some of the drug companies putting out SSRIs were pointing the finger at the other companies and saying their competitors' drugs caused worse problems than their own. Although, to be honest, I didn't see much difference among the brands.

MAN'S GUIDE: **Sounds like they're even better at pointing fingers than at developing new drugs.**

DR. MODELL: The fact is that we should have realized these early figures on sexual problems and SSRI use were a bit too rosy. I mean, you look at the adverse drug effects as reported on the drug's box and in the *Physician's Desk Reference*, and you see something like "5 percent to 25 percent of people experience sexual side effects." Well, when you see a number that low for a problem that's actually pretty common, you should be suspicious. After all, studies have shown that up to about to 40 percent of women and 30 percent of men typically have sexual dysfunction anyway.

MAN'S GUIDE: Great. So if you're depressed, or the woman in your life is depressed, your sex life might have already been in the toilet. Then, the drugs that make you feel better overall make the sex problems worse.

DR. MODELL: But here's the good news: Many of my patients who were on Wellbutrin-SR were reporting to me that their libidos were better than before and their orgasms were better and lasted longer. In some cases, the improvements meant that their sex lives were not only better than when they were depressed, but better than *before* they became depressed.

This piqued our curiosity. So we decided to be a bit more systematic about figuring out what was happening, and we asked 300 of our outpatients some open-ended questions.

You see, one of the problems with past studies on antidepressants and libido is that they either focused on some very limited set of problems or asked vague questions. So we asked very specific questions about things like orgasm duration, orgasm intensity, level of arousal during sexual activity, how quickly people became aroused, how quickly they reached orgasm, and things like that. And we attached specific number scales to these questions so patients could really quantify things.

MAN'S GUIDE: And you found what?

DR. MODELL: Well, approximately 75 percent of the people who were taking SSRIs reported a reduction in one or more of the aspects of sexual functioning we asked about—and often, the problems they experienced were even worse than before they had become depressed.

Now, another interesting point is that when the newest SSRI, Celexa [citalipram hydrobromide], came out, many people were saying that this drug caused significantly fewer sexual side effects than the other SSRIs. I was a bit dubious. And, lo and behold, according to our survey of patients, decreases in one or more areas were reported by about the same percentage of people as on the other drugs.

On the other hand, roughly 75 percent of the people taking Wellbutrin-SR reported *improvement* in one or more of the areas of sexual function. Of course, after we reported this in the literature, we got criticized for doing a retrospective study. People were saying that because we asked about past events, the results would be biased in favor of Wellbutrin-SR, or against the SSRIs.

MAN'S GUIDE: But lots of scientific studies are retrospective. What kind of logic is that?

DR. MODELL: We wondered the same thing, and we decided to do another study, in which we focused on nondepressed people who had reported problems reaching climax in an acceptable amount of time. So this time, it was a *prospective* study, and it had nothing specifically to do with depression. We established a baseline, then we gave these people placebos and Wellbutrin-SR at different points in the study.

In the women, we saw significant improvements from the baseline levels in areas like overall libido, time from arousal to orgasm, duration of orgasm, and intensity of orgasm. In the men, we saw improvement in areas like overall sexual satisfaction, ability to achieve an erection, and time to reach orgasm.

You see, a lot of men and women, when they are on SSRIs, take a long time to go

SEX TRENDS

GIVE IT TO HER STRAIGHT

Men love women with curves. Too bad it isn't the other way around—especially for guys with Peyronie's disease, a condition that causes a painful curvature of the penis. Thankfully, a new prescription medication called topical verapamil has been shown to break down the plaque that causes the curvature and allow healthy tissue to grow in its place. In one study, 71 percent of 214 patients reported a decrease in their curve. For more information, check www.peyronies.com.

from arousal to orgasm. With SSRIs in their systems, it sometimes took so long to get to the point of orgasm that they would just give up trying.

As an interesting little side note, I should mention that SSRIs are predictable enough in terms of how they delay orgasm that they can be used clinically to help treat problems with premature ejaculation.

MAN'S GUIDE: Based on this second study, then, Wellbutrin-SR shows its ability to keep love alive.

DR. MODELL: Yes, but I should note that the people in this study reported improvements in some of these sexual areas even when they were on the placebo as opposed to the real drug. So that shows that some of their problems were not strictly physical. I don't mean that in a negative way, as if I were saying there were no problems—because those problems were very real. But, obviously, it shows that sexual problems have a largely psychological component.

Still, even though patients improved when on placebos, the gains were even more significant after 3 weeks on Wellbutrin-SR, yet they had no idea when they were getting the drug and when they were getting the placebo. So it wasn't all just psychological.

Another intersting aside: Two of the men in our study later decided to try Viagra [sildenafil] to compare its effect with that of Wellbutrin-SR. Perhaps not surprisingly, Viagra was most helpful in solving sexual dysfunction in terms of getting it up, whereas Wellbutrin-SR was better in terms of libido and making the orgasms better and longer.

MAN'S GUIDE: Well, the drugs have one thing in common: Both of them are making something longer.

DR. MODELL: That's the truth. Having said all this, a point does need to be made: Wellbutrin-SR is *not* an aphrodisiac. Not at all.

MAN'S GUIDE: There goes that idea . . .

DR. MODELL: The improvements are significant, that much is clear. Still, although some report large improvements, most will say they had only mild improvement, and some report no changes at all.

And that's fine, as small improvements in these situations can make huge differences in quality of life and enjoyment of sex.

MAN'S GUIDE: If you were starting from zero, you'd think any improvement was fantastic.

> **DR. MODELL:** Very true. The thing is, even if Wellbutrin-SR were able to do what Spanish fly, oysters, and other substances have claimed to be able to do over the years, this is not a drug you can just pop in your mouth and [then] go wild. It can take weeks for the drug to get into your system enough to show the improvement we saw in our patients.
>
> Wellbutrin-SR is fairly safe, but like any drug, it is not completely safe. This is not a substance to be used recreationally. But it might be very useful for a physician in treating sexual dysfunction, even if the patient is not depressed.

MAN'S GUIDE: You noted that some patients reported much larger improvements than others. Did anyone blow the roof off the joint, so to speak?

> **DR. MODELL:** Well, not exactly. But I had one patient, a woman whom I put on Wellbutrin-SR to deal with depression and stress. Her husband, a man in his 60s who had recently been through coronary bypass surgery, asked me to lower her dosage because he couldn't keep up with her increased sex drive.

MAN'S GUIDE: Hey, if you've got to go, we can't think of a better way. But this guy might not want his wife to be *too* frisky.

> **DR. MODELL:** Actually, you bring up a point that is often overlooked by patients and their physicians: It is always best, when treating someone with a sexual problem, to involve the partner and get his or her assessment of the problem and desired treatment outcomes. The man who had the heart surgery is one example of this, but perhaps a more common one we see is when a man comes in to get Viagra for erectile dysfunction, and then we discover that his wife, who had been perfectly content with him leaving her alone, is now irritated that she is supposed to hop-to and perform. You can cause some pretty significant relationship problems that way.

On the other hand, I recall treating a particular couple, both of whom were depressed, and the husband claimed that the wife didn't want sex enough, and she complained that he wanted sex too much. I ended up treating him with an SSRI and her with Wellbutrin-SR, and they met in the middle, so to speak.

MAN'S GUIDE: The middle of the bed, we hope. But obviously, this isn't magic.

DR. MODELL: No. Expectation has a lot to do with all of this sexual stuff. Really, most people on Wellbutrin-SR won't notice the changes outright unless they know what to look for. When we were doing our studies, we knew what to look for and we knew what to ask people to pay attention to. But in real life, people aren't sitting in bed with scorecards and timers rating how long it takes to get to orgasm and how good it was on a scale of one to 10.

It's funny, though, you start thinking about odd things when you study something like this. Do you know that Wellbutrin-SR is the same drug as Zyban, which helps people stop smoking? One might wonder, if Wellbutrin-SR is enhancing your sex life but the drug also curbs smoking, will you want that after-sex cigarette more or less after taking Wellbutrin-SR?

MAN'S GUIDE: If you need research subjects to find out, we have staff who could make time.

DR. MODELL: Well, thanks. But all kidding aside, one thing people need to realize is that a lot of sexual dysfunction out there—and there is plenty of it—is the result of unrecognized depression. So although Wellbutrin-SR might work well on sexual dysfunction even in the absence of depression, if we put a patient on Wellbutrin-SR

hot TIP!

If they had prostate cancer, most prostate specialists confide that they'd burn rubber to a respected research hub—or at least have their doctors consult with the physicians there. Top centers number in the dozens, but these 10 are especially popular choices.

1. Baylor College of Medicine, Houston

2. Duke University, Durham, North Carolina

3. Johns Hopkins University, Baltimore

4. Mayo Clinic, Rochester, Minnesota

5. Memorial Sloan-Kettering Cancer Center, New York City

6. University of California, Los Angeles

7. University of Pennsylvania, Philadelphia

8. University of Texas, M.D. Anderson Cancer Center, Houston

9. Washington University, St. Louis

10. University of Michigan, Ann Arbor

and his or her sex life improves, it may be that we're treating an underlying—and unrecognized—depression more than we're treating the sexual problem directly. Sometimes it is hard to sort out what's what.

MAN'S GUIDE: How do the SSRI makers morally justify their actions? It seems like they swept this whole issue under the rug.

DR. MODELL: I see how it could look like that, but I really don't think that the drug companies were being intentionally deceptive. Early studies on the effects of new drugs often underestimate the true incidence of side effects because the drugs are tested on relatively healthy patients and volunteers, and we don't always know the right questions to ask until we've seen how the drug affects the much larger number of people who take it once it's on the market. I might add, though, that some more recent studies have shown that some depressed people who have sexual problems because of depression actually regain some of their sexual function once the depression is treated with SSRIs. But other studies indicate that there is either little gain in comparison to the sexual function the person was having before the depression, or sometimes even a worsening.

The honest truth is that SSRIs *are* safe and effective. They are good drugs. You simply have to weigh the advantages and disadvantages of them on a patient-by-patient basis.

MAN'S GUIDE: One size doesn't fit all, you mean?

DR. MODELL: That's right. One size rarely fits all.

MAN'S GUIDE: It still seems twisted that depression reduces sex drive, and so does one of its major treatments. What's the physiological explanation for this?

DR. MODELL: It can get pretty complex. The body is regulated by nerve pathways and chemical systems. And really, that's almost the same thing, because nerve pathways involve chemicals called neurotransmitters, which bind to various neuroreceptors.

Sexual function is regulated largely by a neurotransmitter called serotonin. In general, anything that increases serotonin overall will decrease sexual functioning. Depending on the specific type of chemical and how it is received by the body, an increase could be excitatory or it could be inhibitory. In the case of SSRIs, the chemical in question, serotonin, turns the sex drive down.

Wellbutrin-SR, on the other hand, increases levels of the neurotransmitters dopamine and norepinephrine, which are involved in arousal and sexual functioning.

MAN'S GUIDE: So serotonin is an off switch, whereas dopamine and norepinephrine are on switches.

DR. MODELL: Maybe not quite so black and white, but more like a brake and an accelerator. When you increase serotonin, it's like you're pressing down on the brake. When you increase norepinephrine or dopamine, it's like you're pressing down on the accelerator.

What makes it even more complicated is that there are many different types of serotonin receptors, and some of them will actually increase sexual functioning. But the ones most heavily involved with SSRIs tend to reduce sexual function.

Nothing is 100 percent though. I once had a woman on Prozac who had clitoral engorgement and experienced spontaneous little orgasms for no particular reason. Interesting, huh?

MAN'S GUIDE: Maybe not if she's giving a presentation to her boss.

DR. MODELL: True.

MAN'S GUIDE: You mentioned earlier that Wellbutrin-SR is not recreational, nor is it an aphrodisiac. But we saw what happened with Viagra. Young, healthy guys with no problems getting erections took the drug so that they could have woodies all night long. Does the same risk exist here?

DR. MODELL: Of course that risk exists. It's human nature that someone is going to use a drug for the wrong purpose. And that's too bad, because no drug is completely safe, not even one as safe as Wellbutrin-SR. If you use this drug too much for minor problems—or worse yet, nonexistent ones—you will cause more problems than you will solve.

That's what happens when drugs are used indiscriminately, and that's why they should be used carefully, under the supervision of a physician. Just like with Viagra, an excellent drug gets bad press because some fools misuse it. Anything can be misused, whether it's gasoline, lawn mowers, guns, drugs, or whatever. But we have to remember, a bad outcome from misusing a drug is the fault of the person who misused it, not the drug or the manufacturer.

There are, of course, people who probably shouldn't take Wellbutrin-SR. For example, people with seizure disorders or bulimia should not take this drug. The risk of having a seizure because of Wellbutrin-SR use is actually very low, but there is more danger of such an occurrence if you have a history of seizures.

perfect figures

"HONEY? IT'S TIME FOR MY HOURLY HEALTH CHECK."

Percentage of women willing to perform a testicular-cancer check on their partners: 94

MAN'S GUIDE: Any last words on antidepressants and sex drive?

DR. MODELL: Well, I would like to note that other antidepressants besides SSRIs and Wellbutrin-SR do exist. And some of these other drugs are also very kind in terms of not reducing libido. Serzone and Remeron, for example, don't seem to cause sexual dysfunction, but they can cause sleepiness.

MAN'S GUIDE: Great—you can get aroused, but then you'll fall asleep before you get to the good parts.

DR. MODELL: Actually, I've seen that happen. See, when it comes to medications, it's all a question of relative risks versus benefits, and that differs from drug to drug and person to person. So whatever medicine you're taking, be sure you discuss with your doctor its advantages and disadvantages, and any side effects—good or bad—that you might be having.

Remember, the goal of taking a medication is generally to improve the quality of your life, and for most people, that includes being able to enjoy healthy sexual relationships.

QUICKIES

THE ORGASM-CURE FOR HICCUPS

A 40-year-old Israeli man with chronic hiccups tried everything to stop them, including massaging his palate with cotton. Then his doctor suggested he try intercourse. The hiccups stopped right after he ejaculated—and they haven't been back for more than a year. "The sexual stimulation may have had just the right effect on the reflex that causes hiccups," says Roni Peleg, M.D., of Ben-Gurion University of the Negev in Israel.

TEA SAPS SEX DRIVE

Don't take your date to a Chinese restaurant. A cup of tea can destroy your sex drive for the evening. Some foods (such as tea, soy, chickpeas, and certain spices) contain small amounts of phytoestrogens, compounds believed to help protect against cancer and heart disease. But researchers suspect that the estrogen levels in tea are high enough to disrupt male hormones temporarily, causing a loss of libido. Sure, tea still has many health benefits, but you're better off with a cup of coffee; at least it'll lengthen your bedtime stamina. One study showed that coffee before games improved athletes' endurance.

DON'T BE HEIR APPARENT

A study of two-generation cases of testicular cancer found that sons develop the disease at a much younger average age than their fathers—27 years old as opposed to 43. The sons' cancers also tended to be more serious: More than 40 percent had cancers that were more severe; only 10 percent had less-threatening cases. "We believe there is a genetic defect that caused most of these cases," says Richard Peschel, M.D., Ph.D., the study's lead author. "It becomes amplified in the sons." All men should check their testicles monthly. But if your dad had testicular cancer, check more often. Make it an every-Sunday shower habit. And it's vital that you get a physical every year.

ASK THE SEX DOC

Q: *I'm only 36, and* <u>*I often lose my erection before I ejaculate.*</u> *What's causing this?*
—C. J., ATLANTA

A: There might be a leak in one of the veins that trap blood in your penis, so that you're able to achieve an erection, but only temporarily. Though we're not sure what causes the problem (a groin injury might be one explanation), it's a fairly common condition. Some urologists try surgery to fix these leaks, but I don't recommend it. It hasn't been perfected yet and may cause side effects, such as penile numbness. A urologist may recommend a pretty easy fix: an elastic band around the base of your penis to keep the blood trapped in the organ.

Q: <u>*Do you really get an erection when you die?*</u>
—S. R., STATE COLLEGE, PENNSYLVANIA

A: No. "This myth probably dates back to the days of public hangings," says Marc Goldstein, M.D., a urologist at New York Hospital-Cornell Medical Center. "When a man is hanged, his spinal cord snaps, which causes the blood vessels in the lower body to dilate. This can lead to an erection." It may also have given rise to the phrase *well-hung.*

Q: <u>*Ever since I crushed my 20-year smoking habit, my sex drive has*</u> <u>*decreased*</u> *and recently I've begun having problems with impotence. Think there's a connection? What can I do?*
—R. R., FREDERICKSBURG, MARYLAND

A: First the good news: Quitting smoking is going to be great for your sex life. Nicotine is a blood vessel constrictor, meaning it causes hardening of the arteries. As your arteries become harder and narrower they let less blood into your penis, making it harder for you to get an erection. Since you've quit, you've already begun to reverse that process. Congratulations.

perfect figures

THEY CRAMP UP
BEFORE THE FINISH.

Percentage of marathoners
who say the sport hasn't
helped their sex lives:
70

. . . .

Now the bad news: After having smoked for a long period of time, it's possible to suffer some temporary setbacks on the road to recovery. If you smoked for 20 years, it may take your body some time to get used to nicotine not being there anymore. And part of that overall adjustment may be a temporary loss of libido. Think of it as a detox period.

Don't let it get to you. Nicotine has a calming effect on your body, which helps smokers to focus on a subject and not be distracted by thoughts or anxieties. When you give up smoking, your ability to think clearly can also diminish and you may end up feeling unsettled mentally, physically, and sexually. It can make you feel nervous and not yourself, and that also can get in the way of sex. If the problems persist, talk to your doctor about nicotine-replacement therapy to help ease the transition.

The Sex Doc is a fictional character.
The actual advice was provided by a variety of
medical doctors and other qualified experts.

2

SUPERCHARGE
YOUR INNER
HUNK

He's there. Somewhere deep inside you. The guy who knows what shoe color looks best with khakis. The guy who can actually tell hairdressers what kind of cut he wants. The guy who can pick cologne that doesn't clash with his deodorant. Who can tie a perfect Windsor on the first try—every time.

Women love this guy. He's confident, smart, and attractive. Maybe he's a little mysterious. Maybe he marches to his own drummer. Either way, it doesn't matter. He smells good. People notice when he walks into a room. In a nutshell, he has style. And when you get right down to it, that's what women dig far more than sturdy biceps or flashy cars.

The following pages are for that guy, the one inside you. Your job is simple: Make sure he reads them. Then let him out . . . and stay the hell out of his way.

Ways to Hide Body Flaws

It's no accident that Superman slips into something a little more comfortable before he goes off to fight for truth, justice, and the American way. The man knows the power of a great outfit. It's time for you to know it, too. Not only can the right clothes make the good parts of you look good, they can also make the bad parts of you look good. The trick? Finding the solution to your particular style problem.

1 **Double chin.** Stiffen up. "Shirts that have stiff collars will give your face a cleaner line," says Alan Flusser, designer and author of *Style and the Man*. Avoid button-down collars, which are too soft to give your chin the strong line it needs. Also avoid turtlenecks, and stay clean-shaven—stubble will only blur your already blurry lines and draw attention to your chins.

2 **Pencil neck.** Disguise it by loading up on garments with rounded necklines like turtlenecks, crewnecks, and spread-collar dress shirts. The soft lines will cut down on the sharp angle caused by a long neck, says Lenny Marcus, who hides actors' body flaws as the costume supervisor for *General Hospital*.

3 **Big butt.** Slightly longer shirts and sweaters will keep things under wraps, as will jackets without back vents. "Vents can gap open if there's bulk underneath, and they won't lie properly," says Jeff Stone, coauthor of *Chic Simple Men's Wardrobe*.

4 **Skinny butt.** Some might not consider this a problem, but those who can't fill out their pants do. Wear untucked shirts or sweaters that end at the hip, not the waist. "Make sure they're cut straight and have some fullness to them," says Flusser. "Anything clingy defeats the purpose."

5 **Gray hair.** To flatter the salt-and-pepper look, wear dark blue, charcoal gray, black, or white. Avoid pastels—they'll make you look washed out. If you wear eyeglasses, choose black or silver frames.

6 **Built like a female supermodel.** Tall and skinny? Increase your breadth. On top, wear layers, like a sweater over your shirt and tie, says Stone. On the bottom, full-cut, pleated pants with 1¾-inch cuffs (wider than recommended for an average-height guy) will make you look both wider and shorter. And stand up straight. Tall men have a tendency to hunch their shoulders and lean forward—a bad look no matter what you're wearing.

7 **Frequently mistaken for a seventh-grader.** If no one is taking you seriously, whether it's when you propose an idea at work or when you hand the bouncer your ID, you need a more grown-up look. Wear tonal or monochromatic colors, says Marcus. A blue suit and white shirt screams, "I'm just out of school, and this is what I'm supposed to wear." When you're dressing for a night out, wear dark colors and make sure your clothes fit properly—no baggy hip-hop styles.

8 **You're a paleface.** You've probably noticed that some colors look fine on you, while others make you look as if you're on your deathbed. If you have fair skin and dark hair, contrasting colors—like black and red—will look best on you. If both your skin and your hair are light, use muted color combinations. A blue suit and medium-blue shirt, for instance, will complement your complexion without overpowering it, says Flusser.

9 **Beer belly.** Wearing your pants at your waist, not under the gut? Good. But a proper fit will only help so much. To further de-emphasize your gut, draw the eye away from it. Wear a V-neck sweater or a shirt with a contrasting (and preferably lighter) collar.

10 **Big head.** You're in good company—Cary Grant had a melon head, too. But he still looked great, thanks to clothing scaled a little bit bigger. Go for broader-cut jacket shoulders and wider ties. Giving off the image of a bigger body will shrink your head.

MUST READS

Whisker Wisdom: How to Shave Your Face

We'll give 10-to-1 odds it was your old man who first taught you how to shave. And you're probably still doing it the way he showed you. Wet, lather, stroke, rinse. Truth is, shaving is less a grooming habit than a ritual—passed down from generation to generation as a rite of passage to manhood.

No offense to your ancestors, but what the heck did they know about the science of shaving? Wouldn't you want to know if there was a better way to shave—a way that didn't leave you nicked, scratched, burned, or covered with rough spots? Here, Wallace G. Pinfold tells you what your father didn't.

Every man shaves in a different fashion. And although individual techniques vary, shavers have a common goal that, like the incest taboo and the prevalence of gravity, is practically universal: a clean shave, a close shave, a shave that doesn't cause suffering while it's being performed or shame and humiliation when it's finished. Mood, temperament, and the circumstances may influence the way a man shaves on a given day, but the basic principles of a good shave are plain and simple.

The Perfect Wet Shave

1. Soften your beard with water. Go for a swim. Stand in the shower for 5 minutes. Soak a washcloth in warm water and apply it to your face, go do something else, then come back and repeat the procedure. The point is to give your whiskers time to get wet enough to swell up a bit; they'll shear off more easily, and your razor blade will last longer.

    If you have a tough beard or sensitive skin, standing in the shower is a particularly good idea. It's a perfect place to shave, especially if you have a nonfogging mirror in there with you.

2. If your beard is really soft and your blade really sharp, you can shave with hot water alone. Applying shaving foam, gel, or cream keeps the beard wet and makes it easier for the razor to glide over the surface of your skin without cutting it. So does plain old soap, albeit less effectively.

3. The conventional wisdom is that long, smooth strokes produce better results than short, jerky ones, and that shaving with the lie of the beard

is better than shaving against it. Every man has to find the method that suits him best; however, some basics do apply. You want to rinse the razor regularly so the blade doesn't clog with soap and stubble, and you should put in a new blade once the one you've been using for the last week to 10 days starts to drag.

For Contrarians

The shaving method patented in 1942 by New York inventor Peter N. Peters may be of interest to those of you who want to break all the rules. Mr. Peters recommended washing, lathering, and rinsing the face with cold water, but shaving with a hot blade—as hot as bearable. Rather than making long, clean strokes with the razor, he suggested making sharp, rapid ones. The reasoning behind the invention was that hot water and lathering make the skin flabby and render the hair so limp it cannot be properly sheared off by the razor.

Ideally, you should go over each area a single time, but the odds are good that you will have missed a patch here or there. Unless your skin is broken out or chronically sensitive, it won't hurt to make a second pass over these patches at a different, crosswise angle. Most beards are toughest on the upper lip and the chin, so leave these for last.

4 Once you're satisfied with the shave, rinse with cold water, pat your face dry, and apply some kind of aftershave product. The choice is up to you, but the same skin-care experts who caution against shaving with painfully hot water or shaving too closely say you shouldn't put alcohol on your skin. You aren't doing your face any favors if it's stinging. After all, you've just shaved off a thin slice of epidermis, and an aftershave that burns is nature's way of letting you know the slice wasn't thin enough. Having just scraped your skin, you want to soothe it, not slap it.

Shaving with an Electric Shaver

Electric shavers have either a rotary head (circular cutters that rotate behind round combs) or a foil head (blades that move back and forth and are covered by one or more flexible metal foils). You move a foil shaver up and down your face; and a rotary shaver in a circular motion. Foil heads have to be replaced fairly often; a rotary head may last for years. Either type can have adjustable settings to regulate the closeness of the shave.

Shaving with an electric shaver has its merits. Your face stays dry, you can shave almost anywhere you like, and unless you're borderline obsessive-compulsive and go over your face again and again and again, you can't even get razor burn.

The drawbacks? Electric shavers cost more, and no matter what you read or see on television, men with tough beards will never get as close a shave with an electric shaver as with a wet razor. Some tips for either option:

● Shave against the lie of your beard and don't press down hard. If the shaver you're using generates a little heat and you have sensitive skin, shave the most tender areas first, before the shaver heats up.

● If your skin is oily, use a pre-shave preparation that will dry up surface moisture and ready your whiskers to be mowed down. A dry and therefore brittle hair is more susceptible than a wet one to the shearing action of an electric shaver.

● Keep your shaver clean. On foil shavers, you can usually lift off the head frame that holds the screen and brush the whisker dust from the underside. Below the screen is the cutter; this part has to be brushed off with the manufacturer's cleaning brush.

● Same drill with a rotary shaver. Once a week (or more often if necessary), brush whiskers from the comb slots. Then lift off the razor head assembly and brush hair from the underside of the three cutters and the razor chamber. Don't rap the heads on the sink to get whiskers out—you may damage the instrument.

● If you're switching from one brand of shaver to another or from wet to dry, give your face time to adjust. It may take 2 to 3 weeks before you get the most your electric shaver has to offer.

Further Dos and Don'ts

● If you have sensitive skin, try an electric shaver first to get rid of the major stubble. Then go back with a wet razor and a light touch to get the closer shave an electric shaver doesn't give. Since it's partly the drag of the razor across the skin that's irritating, make as

hot TIP!

Wanna shave your pate without leaving stray tufts sprouting like ornamental grasses? Try the HeadBlade. This $15 razor hooks around your middle finger so you can easily shave your whole head. Call (877) 427-2067.

few passes as possible. Over the weekend, give your face a rest from shaving.

● If your skin has a tendency to break out or you nick easily, choose an alcohol-free, unscented aftershave balm. Also, using a moisturizer at night will make shaving easier for you the next morning. Don't shave immediately after rolling out of bed. You've been horizontal all night long, and body fluids have pooled and puffed up the surface of your skin. Wait a few minutes while this puffiness dissipates.

Rough around the Edges

A man who maintains a 3-day growth of stubble for weeks or months on end does not achieve that look with an electric razor—he uses electric clippers set on the lowest setting. Stubble works on a man's face the way contouring makeup works on a woman's, creating shadows and definition absent from his clean-shaven visage.

Stubble makes you look as if you just got out of bed, which can be read as (1) kinda sexy or (2) kinda disoriented. Whichever message you wish to send, don't contradict it with overly neat edges. Stubble's message is "I'm hipper than most and I've got better things to do than shave." So do them—and leave those edges alone.

● In an ideal world, we'd shave in the evening when the face is oilier and its owner is less rushed.

● In general, you want to shave when you skin is least likely to suffer from irritation. Shave in the evening in the summer. Sunscreen, chlorine from the pool, or salt from the ocean may irritate freshly showered skin. Don't shave just before you work out; perspiration is highly alkaline and can make dry skin drier. Besides, you'll get a better shave after the postworkout shower.

● If any mention of skin care causes your testosterone level to drop, you can pick up a bottle of witch hazel at the drugstore for a little over a dollar. It's 14 percent alcohol, pleasantly astringent, and also good for mosquito bites.

Razor Bumps

Good preparation, a decent razor, and a modicum of attention to skin care will result in a satisfactory shave for most men. Men with coarse, curly beards will have a harder time of it. Sooner or later, they're likely to develop the annoying condition known as razor bumps (*Pseudofolliculitisbarbae*, or PFB). The condition is particularly severe among African-American men and men of southern Mediterranean origin.

PFB results when the barbed tip of a newly shorn beard hair curls back on itself and penetrates the surface of the skin. The body treats the hair as a foreign body, and infection sets in. The resulting bump or bumps get nicked with every pass of the razor, aggravating the condition.

There's no cure, but there are remedies. One remedy is to grow a beard. If personal preference or professional considerations make that solution unfeasible, another is to use an electric razor specifically designed for the problem.

If you are predisposed to PFB but still prefer a wet razor, here are some precautions you can take to avoid ingrown hairs in the first place.

● Use an exfoliant. Massage the beard area in small circular motions with either a clean, soft toothbrush or a facial scrub. This motion sets up beard hairs to be shaved, dislodges hairs starting to grow in the wrong direction, and gets rid of dead cells at the same time. Better yet, plan ahead. Use a moisturizer that contains AHA, a natural fruit acid that does the same thing as a facial scrub, just a bit less vigorously.

● Dip your razor in alcohol before you shave.

● Shave with the grain.

● If you've shaved over an ingrown hair and it's become infected, use an antibacterial agent like salicylic acid. Once the infection has cleared up, the hair should release itself. But stop shaving this patch until your skin has healed.

● Use a translucent shaving cream; it will allow you to see sensitive areas and avoid reinjury.

● If you don't have to be perfectly clean-shaven, don't lean on the blade so hard. Try leaving a little whisker. Or shave at night: your face will have the whole night to recover from your mistakes.

● If shaving continues to be a problem, try using a depilatory. But be careful; some can irritate skin that's already raw.

● If none of this works, rethink a beard.

Score Style Points in the Dating Game

Many men suffer from the delusion that good looks, great lines, and a decent amount of charm—well, at least two out of the three, anyway—are enough to attract women. Wrong. You care how a woman packages herself, right? Well, she cares how you're packaged, too.

To get you up to speed on the basics of how to dress like a winner in this high-stakes game, writer Jeffrey Bouley consulted the Men's Health *magazine style pages and spoke with two men who know the playing field well: Christopher Rovny, vice president of marketing and weekly fashion columnist for www.askmen.com, and Bruce Boyer, the author of three books on men's fashion and a freelance writer for magazines such as* Men's Health, Departures, *and* Forbes. *Here's how to package·yourself as a must-have man.*

In order to attract a woman—whether for long-term love or just for the night—you want to come across as comfortable in your own skin. In other words, you don't want to dress too young or too old. Above all, you don't want to look like a slob. Because if you don't pay attention to the details, you might have to watch as some ho-hum guy walks away with the sexy prize you had your eye on.

Plot your moves with this age-by-age guide.

The 20s

Express your originality and show a sense of style, but don't go overboard on eccentricity. Add an original touch to a classic look. "Wearing the right clothes can make the difference between spending a Saturday night smooching with a blond bombshell and renting a movie you have already seen twice," says Rovny.

Advance three spaces with these in your closet . . .

❶ Nice jeans that fit well

Steer clear of designer labels at this point in life; they will hurt your pocketbook and may not fit any better than a good pair from the Gap or Old Navy. If you can afford a second pair, buy them in black.

Style point: Jeans are worn at your hips, not an inch above your belly button. And they shouldn't break on top of the shoe—they should just brush the middle of the laces.

❷ Casual, Dockers-style pants and chinos

Style point: The warmer the temperature, the more shades of khaki you can wear. Spring khakis should be no lighter than medium tan. In summer, wear any color. By October, khakis should be darker again.

● Trendy shoes

Even if they're sneakers, try to go with a clear "brand" name here. Black leather shoes with squared-off toes and lug soles work well at this age, and you can't go wrong with a nice pair of brown suede shoes from a store or a company that uses high-quality leather.

● Nice-fitting crew neck and V-neck shirts

Buy an assortment of long- and short-sleeved. A good V-neck, especially a long-sleeved one, can make even a skinny guy look more buff.

Style point: Keep two piles of T-shirts: one for sweating and one for dating.

● All-cotton polo and button-down shirts

Whatever color you choose, make sure you're comfortable being seen in it.

Style point: If you have a round face, choose pointed collars to lengthen it. For a long face, the spread collar will round you out.

After the Game Shows, Watch the Soaps

Fashions change, and no resource—not even this one—can cover all the bases. How can you keep up? How can you know what women really like? According to Allen Thompson, editor of the *Don Juan Newsletter* and head of the Don Juan Center (at www.SoSuave.com), you can find all your answers in the soap operas.

"Personally, I hate soap operas," he is quick to point out. "But you have to remember, these things were designed for women, so the men on these shows are always extremely well-dressed—even in casual attire.

"The colors, the styles, how it all fits together—you can never go wrong."

For the sake of your sanity, Thompson recommends taping several shows while you're at work and making liberal use of the fast-forward button when you get home. Find characters around your age, who share some of your characteristics (or possess ones you'd like to cultivate), and have a similar build and coloring. Follow their leads, to the extent that your wallet can handle it.

If you can't afford the full-on soap look, buy a few classic (or sexy, or whatever is most important to you) key items you have identified. And no matter what you do, don't let your buddies see those videos hanging around your place.

● At least one blazer
A real one, in navy blue with silver- or gold-colored, blazer-style buttons. Go for the most quality you can afford. You can pair this with jeans, trousers, or suit pants—and impress women equally well.

● Your first suit
Make your first suit a black one. You can wear it to a party with a festive shirt, and to nondate outings like job interviews or funerals.

● Leather or suede
Leather jackets can be stylish or can project that "bad boy" image if that's what you're going for. Suede camp-style shirts (two front pockets) can give you an air of "cool."

   Style point: Wear this shirt untucked over a nice crew-neck T-shirt.

perfect figures

HE WAS NO
WILT CHAMBERLAIN.

Number of women with whom legendary lover Casanova is reputed to have had sexual relations: 132

● Accessories
Wear whatever style of watch suits you, and if an earring works on you, great. If you have a penchant for canvas or hemp wallets, fine—just make sure you have enough cash in there *before* you go out.

Or go back to START with this stuff in your wardrobe . . .

● Rock-group T-shirts
In the real world, Tia Carrere wouldn't be caught dead with Wayne.

● Baggy clothes
Don't go there, unless you're in P. Diddy's posse.

● Nylon and other synthetic materials
Very few people look good in these. But you can never go wrong with cotton, linen, or wool.

The 30s

Boyer says that the 30s are a time when "much is forgiven." Specifically, you can still get away with dressing like you're in your 20s, while also refining your look to add more style and class. Adding that sense of class—while increasing the quality and cost of your clothes—is critical to show that you are moving up in

Don't Sink Your Own Battleship: Classic Style Missteps

Certain style points—and style mistakes—transcend age. Here we offer the five biggest errors that will undermine your strategy.

1. **Too-short pants.** Toss your high-waters. This look doesn't even pass on 10-year-old boys at British boarding schools. Your date shouldn't be able to see your socks, unless you have a leg crossed or you're in the process of getting ready for bedroom activities. Which brings us to . . .

2. **Old underwear.** Think a dirty, ragged pair will set the right mood? It won't. So consider carefully what you put on underneath. There's no particular advantage with regard to briefs versus boxers—wear what's comfortable for you. But style does matter. A younger guy can get away with silly patterned boxers or colorful briefs; otherwise, tone it down. And leave the bikini briefs alone, unless you're *Baywatch* material.

3. **White socks.** Don't wear them except during honest-to-God athletic activities. Worn in dating mode, they scream, "I still live with my mom!" Also, avoid wearing socks that are too light or too dark compared to your shoes and pants.

4. **Too much cologne.** Overdoing the cologne suggests you forgot to shower or have no style what-soever. Also be aware that the seasons may dictate what you dab on your face and neck (or wherever else you dab). Heavier musk scents are better for winter and fall; lighter citrus scents work well in spring and summer.

5. **Subpar personal hygiene.** Shower, keep your breath always fresh, trim your mustache and beard, clip your nose hairs, clean your ears. You don't have to look like a model; just look like you care. Shaving is a bit more age-specific than other hygiene issues. A guy in his 20s or early 30s may look like a stud with a few days' growth of whiskers. An older man who doesn't shave his stubble regularly looks like a bum.

the world. Or, as Rovny wrote in a recent e-mail, "Remember, many women in this age group are looking for their '$oul mates.'"

Pass GO and collect $200 . . .
❍ Upgrade some of those chinos to linen/silk-blend trousers.
Style point: If your girth is too substantial for flat fronts, go with a pleat or two, no more. And don't carry your keys in your pants pocket. The jangling sound is not a plus. More important, the keys wreck the smooth line you're after.

❍ Start accessorizing with a decent leather wallet and a nicer watch.
Style point: Match the color of your metal watch with the color of your belt buckle and any metal on your shoes.

❍ Start buying designer jeans.
Make sure they fit well—not too tight, not too baggy.

❍ Get a few nicely tailored suits.
Don't cheap out; buy the best suits you can afford.
   Style point: Some suit jackets can be worn without matching pants, but be careful: Solids occasionally work solo, but richly textured suit jackets are best at succeeding on their own.

Don't be "Sorry!" with these . . .
❍ Hawaiian shirts
These and other eccentric shirts don't work with women in their 30s, unless they're air-headed, bleached-blonde surfer bums themselves.

❍ Trendy shoes
Replace them with classy, higher-quality footwear. Air Jordans won't fly on a date with a 30-something woman.
   Style point: Suede and nubuck shoes stain easily, so don't leave the store without a can of protective spray. Coat the shoes before you wear them outside.

The 40s
Now is the time to show you pay attention to details. "Accessories become much more important," Boyer says. "Guys in their 40s who look good are the guys who pay attention to haircuts, eyeglass frames, shoes, belts, and types of fabric. All of a sudden, you get in to your 40s and become more aware of the words cashmere, vicuna, camel hair, and mohair."

Get a free spin with . . .

◉ Good-quality suits

Even if you date a decade or two below your own age, this is the way to go. As Rovny reminds us, "Women just love older men." You'll look silly if you try to emulate Leonardo DiCaprio.

◉ A sharp, classy watch

Style point: Got a gold watch? Make your second one silver. Or try a pocket watch.

◉ Conservative colors and patterns

Wear them.

◉ A belt arsenal

Style point: You want a brown, a black, and a cordovan (the maroon leather that looks great with navy and gray). You need two casual woven belts (black and brown) for informal occasions, and a canvas belt to keep your jeans up. Match the shoes in color and finish: Shiny shoes with shiny belt; suede/buck shoes with matte-finished belt.

◉ A high-quality wallet, a nice case for your palmtop computer, etc.

For these leather accessories, consider exotic animal skins (but stay off the endangered species lists, unless you want to look heartless and crass).

◉ A cell phone of the sleek, stylish, and very small variety

Style point: Turn it off during a date.

◉ French cuffs and cuff links

Resist conventional wisdom, including the cliché that French cuffs and cuff links should be worn only with suits on very formal occasions.

   Style point: If you're wearing a sport coat, slacks, and a tie, and it's dark outside, a little glitter at the wrists adds some dash.

Or go directly to jail for wearing these . . .

◉ Really bright colors

Keep your brights to one per ensemble, and understand that they work better on the golf course than on a date.

◉ Chunky shoes with thick soles and squared-off toes

Not even shoes will take you back to your 20s.

◉ Trendy clothes

Avoid almost anything worn by 20-year-olds on billboards or in magazine ads. Rovny insists they will make you look creepy.

● **A comb-over**

If you're balding, accept it (and that means no hairpieces, either). They fool no one, least of all women. In a survey of more than 2,000 women for *What Women Want* (Rodale, 2000), 91 percent of them said men shouldn't worry if they start losing their hair.

The 50s and Beyond

Time to hike up your waistband and don black socks with sandals? Uh, no. (For the record, that time never comes.)

"Your retirement years should be some of the best years of your life," Rovny insists. "Women in their 50s like confident and active men. Wear clothes that are comfortable, elegant, and classy at the same time."

Rethink your accessories, too. Cuff links are still a good option, but maybe those horn-rimmed eyeglasses are not—especially if your hair is thinning (or completely AWOL). If you wear glasses and your hair is sparse, thin wire rims are often a good choice.

Consider these your "get out of jail free" cards . . .

● **Subdued colors and subtle patterns**

Remember, we said subdued and subtle, not sepulchral and somber. If you're reading this, you aren't dead yet, you aren't Amish, and you probably aren't a Roman Catholic priest.

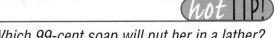

Which 99-cent soap will put her in a lather? We asked a dozen women to sniff and resniff the freshly washed body of one of our staffers (the women signed a waiver). Here's how they rated the scents.

SOAP	RATING	WHAT SHE SAID
Lever 2000	★★★★★	"Strong, clean, subtle. Oh baby, take it off."
Irish Spring Sport	★★★★	"An athletic man. Hope he's as good as he smells."
Shield	★★★★	"Outdoorsy. You definitely know he showered."
Dial	★★★½	"Smells like he likes to chop wood."
Coast	★★★	"Strong and cologne-ish. A little fruity."
Irish Spring	★★★	"Smells like a frat party."
Zest	★★	"Smells like the hand wash in doctors' offices."
Ivory	★★	"He just did the dishes."
Tone	★½	"Like pollen. Makes me want to sneeze."
Safeguard	★	"Like detergent or fruitcake."
Dove	½	"Guy lives with his parents or grandparents."

● **Plenty of elegant and comfortable cotton pants and cotton tops**
Style point: For the best fit, sit down when you try the pants on. Since your waist and hips get bigger when you sit, if the pants are too small, you'll be uncomfortable in a sitting position. And when it comes to knit polo shirts, for a dressier look, wear the shirt closed at the neck.

● **Several good-looking, warm, wool sweaters for the cooler seasons**
Style point: Heavy sweaters should be roomy—nice and loose where the arms meet the body and across the chest. Thinner sweaters worn under a jacket should be more form-fitting, the armholes a tad tighter. Sweaters should fall below your waist to your hipbones: too short and you could be mistaken for a figure skater.

● **At least one pair of nice loafers**
Make sure they have minimal hardware and tassels.
     Style point: Loafers are great with khakis or jeans, or maybe a sport coat. Just don't wear them with a suit—this is an occasion that cries out for laces or buckles.

Or lose a turn with these . . .
● **Bright colors and bold patterns**
Do you really want women to remember your clothes (and laugh at them) rather than remember you? If you're dating at this stage of the game, we hope not—it's tough enough out there already.

● **Baggy clothes**
Though you may need a looser fit to camouflage weight gain.

● **Cutting-edge fashions**
Wearing the waistband of your pants down around your knees and a baseball cap backwards will not look the same on you as on a 20-year-old. Trust us.

The Guide to Taking It Off

Next time you're in the locker room, watch a guy take his clothes off (or rather, sneak a glimpse on the sly—unless you enjoy the taste of painted steel). Remind you of anything? Nothing you'd want to remember, we'll bet. The truth is, men suck at disrobing. Between tripping over pant legs and getting stuck in turtlenecks, it's a wonder that women who witness it stick around. Put a little effort into it, man. Trust us, she'll reward you.

When our partners dragged us to see *The Full Monty* a couple of years ago, we expected to be repulsed by eyeful after eyeful of lumpy, misshapen Englishmen. In fact, the mere premise of unemployed factory employees baring their pasty skin to make ends meet struck us as decidedly unsexy. Our partners? They couldn't get enough. In fact, they were so caught up in watching men try to be sexy that they didn't notice the men weren't succeeding. "It goes to show you that sex doesn't have to be serious or even sexy. If those five guys can be a turn-on, so can any middle-aged or out-of-shape man in America," says Michael Seiler, Ph.D., a marital and sexual therapist in private practice in Chicago.

perfect figures

AND THE REST
ARE WAITING FOR YOU.

Percentage of women who say
they could be romanced
by a man who's less
than perfect: 80

That gave us an idea. So we called Billy Dean, a male stripper and owner of Billy Dean's Male Dance Revue in Long Island, New York, and asked for a few pointers on how even lumpy, misshapen Americans like ourselves might be able to pull off a similar stunt in the privacy of our bedrooms.

"I think it's a great idea and perhaps the ultimate foreplay," says Susan Crain Bakos, a sexologist and author of *Sexsational Secrets*. "It's the perfect way to help revitalize a sexual relationship that may be starting to get stale."

Studies from the Netherlands show that, contrary to popular belief, visual stimulation is an important component of arousal for women. In fact, when researchers hooked women up to special vaginal devices that measure genital bloodflow, then showed them clips from erotic films, they found the women's arousal increased at levels comparable to men's.

In other words, there's a good chance your partner won't be able to keep her hands off you by the time you're done stripping. Even if it goes badly, take heart—laughter is also an aphrodisiac. "It's not always the worst thing to make a little bit of a fool of yourself," reassures Bakos. Best of all, the performance will appeal to your exhibitionist tendencies and get both of you warmed up.

Setting the Mood

Since you won't have an audience of 400 screaming women to produce ambience, it's up to you to create the sexy but energetic atmosphere that'll be key to pulling off your act.

◦ Pick a character.

There's nothing wrong with plain old you, but when it comes to performance sex, a little creativity can go a long way. Find out what she fantasizes about, then act it out. Don't limit yourself to the standbys of the entertainment business: policemen, naval officers, mechanics, cowboys, and construction workers. If she really wants a stockbroker, dust off the suspenders.

◦ Dress up.

Once you've chosen your character, chances are you can fashion a costume from the clothes in the back of your closet. Just remember that when you want to get undressed without getting tangled up, snaps work better than buttons (professionals even have tailors replace seams in their pants with Velcro so they can rip them off in one swoop). Or to go all out, check your phone book for a local costume shop.

> " There we were in the middle of a sexual revolution wearing clothes that guaranteed we wouldn't get laid. "
>
> —Denis Leary

Whatever you pick, keep in mind that it's not going to stay on for very long anyway. "More important than what you start out in is what you end up in," says Bakos. Not every guy can pull off the traditional G-string or thong. Try a sexy pair of snug, colorful briefs instead.

◦ Set the lighting.

In *The Full Monty*, spotlights tracked the dancers so the audience could see every move (and every awkward body part) in clear detail. You probably don't have stage lighting in your bedroom—and it's just as well. Soft lighting, say, from a bedside reading lamp, can help trick her into believing you really do have the body of a stripper. Candles also work well.

◦ Don't forget cologne.

To make your performance a treat for as many senses as possible, place a dab of sexy cologne on your chest before getting dressed. As soon as your shirt comes off, she'll get a whiff.

◦ Turn on the tunes.

Try to picture the boys from Monty without Tom Jones's "You Can Leave Your Hat On." "It's important to pick something slow and likable. A lot of novices make the mistake of using music that's too fast and hard to dance to," says Dean. Your best bet is a classic sexy song with a heavy beat, such as Hot Chocolate's "You Sexy Thing." Or try one of her favorite artists—even if the music is harder to dance to, you'll score big points just for jazzing up "her" song.

Time to Take It Off

You've got everything you need, including one very intrigued partner. Now for the hard part: the act itself.

PERFORMANCE ANXIETY?

Percentage of men who wouldn't want to stand in for a male movie star during a sex scene: 79

● **Take it slow.**

You're not in the locker room and you won't win any points for efficiency here. In fact, a good striptease is as much about what you don't reveal as what you do. "Women are turned on by a slow, integrated experience, taking it one step at a time. The more you can drag out the anticipation, the more exciting it's going to be for her," says Seiler. Teasing is essential—change your mind often. Ideally, she'll never really know for sure if you plan on going through with it.

● **Make eye contact.**

Every professional stripper worth the tips in his G-string knows this secret. "It's absolutely essential, even if you feel shy. Looking right into her eyes conveys a sense of sexual confidence that's sure to be a turn-on," says Bakos.

● **Stay in motion.**

Okay, you're not a dancer. Believe us, neither are we. But we managed. The trick? Stick with slow, easy, graceful motions. Sway your hips in time to the music and punctuate the heaviest beats with pelvic angling. Keep your arms in motion and tease playfully with your removed clothing before discarding it. Keep in mind you don't have to get all serious and seductive like the models in underwear catalogs. "If your enthusiasm is high and you're really aiming to please, that will make up for any lack of sensual movement," says Dean.

● **Solicit audience participation.**

Strip clubs strictly enforce the "look but don't touch" rule. Not so at your place: Feel free to solicit assistance from your audience of one. In fact, it could come in handy when you get down to the trickier operations like sliding those tight jeans over your ankles. "Just don't let her forget who's in control. Keep in mind that it's your job to entertain her, not vice versa," says Dean.

> **"** Sex appeal is 50 percent what you've got and 50 percent what people think you've got. **"**
>
> —Sophia Loren

⊙ Use props.

One of the dancers in Dean's club uses a half-cantaloupe in his act. "He places it on the stage in front of him, then falls down onto it so it looks like he's eating it the same way he would pleasure his wife," says Dean. That may not be your style, but be creative with the objects around you—and on you—and she's likely to play along.

⊙ Get her naked, too.

If you time things right, you'll be all the way down to your skivvies just in time for the music to die down. The show may be over, but that's no reason to bring the curtain down. Switch to a slower song, then pull her into the act and help her out of those clothes.

THE FUNNY PAGE

"Capri pants, capri jacket—the ideal summer suit."

HELP ONLINE

CUTTING COSTS

If you're considering teeth bleaching, LASIK eye surgery, or another
elective surgery—like, say, a bunionectomy—check out this site.
You post your request for an operation, and local surgeons submit their bids.
If you accept a bid, you'll be scheduled for an appointment to talk
to the doctor—after you check his credentials online.
www.medicineonline.com/bidforsurgery

THE SPIFF-UP SPOT

An ultra-hip online purveyor of premium men's grooming products, tips,
expert advice, and the latest news and views on men's style. The products they
offer include shaving essentials, skincare, hair care, fragrances, and more.
www.mankindonline.co.uk

MAKEUP FOR MEN?

On the Internet there's something for everyone. Want to wear mascara
and sport a manicure? This is the site for you. Male Species caters
to the growing male interest in cosmetics and skin care products.
Based in Las Vegas (where else?), they offer quality men's cosmetics,
skin care products, and stage makeup for entertainers and models.
They've got everything from shaving cream to blush, body glitter
to nail finish. Best of all, you won't need to skulk through
the drugstore makeup aisle anymore.
www.malespecies.com

MAN'S GUIDE INTERVIEW

Women Want Regular Guys: Secrets from America's Top Bachelors

An Interview with Seth Berkley, M.D., and Neil Willenson

What does it take to be considered attractive by women? Do you need chiseled abs, lots of money, a thick head of hair? Possibly. Some women wet their pants over that stuff.

And we'll admit it: men's publications like ours help perpetuate that notion. We spend a lot of time telling you how to sculpt your body, save your money, keep your hair. And we strongly believe those are good things to do. A healthy bank account and body will take you far. Still, we can't help but wonder if there isn't something more.

So we asked people.

People magazine, *that is. Turns out the women they polled rate good looks and money last on a list of male attributes that starts with sense of humor, sensitivity, and intelligence. Then, just to make ourselves feel even more shallow, we talked to two of the men* People *picked in 2001 as part of their "sexy, single, sizzling" top-50 bachelors.*

Bachelor Number One: Seth Berkley, M.D., 44, the president and chief executive officer of the International AIDS Vaccine Initiative in New York City, which is working to develop vaccines to eradicate HIV infection and AIDS worldwide. Bachelor Number Two: Neil Willenson, 30, the founder of nonprofit Camp Heartland, which serves more than 600 kids and teens affected by HIV or AIDS at a year-round facility in Willow River, Minnesota, and a summer-only camp in Malibu, California.

These guys are regular guys. Just like you. Not model-handsome, not tycoon-rich (they work in the nonprofit sector, for crying out loud). And clearly, they have what women want. Do you? Keep reading and find out.

MAN'S GUIDE: How did you guys *really* feel when you found out you were included among the country's top-50 bachelors?

BERKLEY: I actually thought it was funny. This country is so obsessed with Hollywood and various movie and media stars. I am clueless on this subject area, as I don't even own a television. Still, I was delighted that they were going to feature some people who actually did some good—as well as who were interesting.

WILLENSON: Overall, I have been flattered. But I am also embarrassed by the attention. As the founder of Camp Heartland, I'm heading up a national charity that makes a profound, lifelong difference in the lives of children impacted by HIV and AIDS. I am surrounded by children who face a number of daily obstacles with great courage and resilience. It has been an absolute privilege to work with the children who come to Camp Heartland.

MAN'S GUIDE: So you think that this "honor," dubious though it may be, was somehow undeserved?

WILLENSON: Well, first off, I am not a good judge if I am "sexy" or "sizzling." So I don't know if I deserved it from that standpoint.

It's just that with the work I do, anything else I do, like dating—or anything I am perceived to be, like one of the top-50 bachelors in the country—pales in comparison. This publicity about my single status seems superficial when I'm dealing with children who have AIDS. I'm not entirely complaining—any publicity for the camp is appreciated and useful.

MAN'S GUIDE: Why do you both think you were included?

BERKLEY: I guess I caught their attention because of my work on AIDS vaccines through the International AIDS Vaccine Initiative, which I head up. That is a pretty high-profile position. In fact, I have been described as an "angry man" with regard to the subject of AIDS vaccines and AIDS research in general, as I cannot believe that the world at large has responded in such an anemic way to the greatest plague since the 14th century.

But it's not all about my work. I think they were also caught by my passion for playing. I fly, dive, sail, ride, run, bike, climb—really active kinds of things.

WILLENSON: *People* seemed to make an effort to include individuals from many walks of life. In a sense, I represent those men who work in the nonprofit sector. I just happen to be more visible than some. I imagine I was included based on the past notoriety of our charity and the uniqueness of the camp—and, of course, the fact that I am single.

MAN'S GUIDE: What would have been the biggest reasons to not have included you on this list? Were there any glaring character flaws *People* missed? Anything you think should have disqualified you?

BERKLEY: I might have disqualified myself given my complete disgust of the celebrity game. I have met some of the most famous people in the world—but so what? My question when I meet people is always this: Are they interesting, compassionate, and nice? Those are the traits that truly matter.

WILLENSON: All I can say is that for me to be included, it must have been slim pickings this year.

Seriously, though, working with children who have AIDS has kept my ego firmly in check. I am surrounded by hundreds of children who struggle for acceptance, understanding, and compassion.

MAN'S GUIDE: What traits do you feel made you deserve recognition as someone in whom women should be interested?

WILLENSON: I feel no greater than any other man. But I do my best to live my life with integrity and purpose. I am certain many men to whom women might be attracted have similar traits.

BERKLEY: Well, when you look at my life, I guess there is that combination of being a person who likes to have fun and is interesting, and who pursues worthwhile enterprises with all of his energy. That would seem to be a nice combination for a discriminating woman.

What I think is interesting about my appearance in this issue of *People* is that certainly I am no great hunk. I don't have washboard abs; I'm not the person you'd put on the front of *Men's Health* or *Playgirl*. On the other hand, I fly, I dive, I sail, I jump horses. I do tons of other different interesting things. I've lived all over the world, and I have lots of great interests that are fun to do and to share.

So I would say that from an intellectual/fun quotient, I would be an interesting companion. And the challenge, I think, is that these are not things people have looked at traditionally. Instead, people have looked at, "If he's in the movies, he must just be great."

To me, the exciting transition in life is people being valued for what they do, what they care about, and whether they are interesting—versus an interest in pure, straight fame, which are the kind of people Americans seem to chase after—mentally at least.

MAN'S GUIDE: Have your phones been ringing off the hook with calls from women determined enough to track you down? And has your life—in general or dating-wise—changed substantively since the issue hit news-stands?

> **BERKLEY:** No and no. I assume that many women thought I was gay, given that my work—and the topic for which I am so passionate—revolves around AIDS.

> **WILLENSON:** Prior to *People*, the camp and I had been profiled a number of times by the national media. So, typically, I would receive a number of calls, e-mails, and letters from people interested in volunteering for our charity or making financial contributions. Following the publication of that *People* issue, I received approximately 100 inquiries from women.

> Admittedly—and I am blushing—a number of women have been interested in a date or a relationship. Still, others want to get involved in the Camp Heartland cause. I am grateful for all those who contact me, but as I have a girlfriend, I am even happier with those who want to support children with AIDS than with those who want a date.

MAN'S GUIDE: Now that you've mentioned your girlfriend, I have to ask: How is she taking your new "hunky" celebrity status?

> **WILLENSON:** I'm not sure about the hunky part. But when I informed my girlfriend of my inclusion in the bachelor issue, she didn't believe me at first. Her initial shock has evolved into enjoyment and support for my participation, and she's glad that a number of people have expressed their interest in the camp as a result. The local media have asked her to comment, but she has decided to stay very discreet. She prefers anonymity.

MAN'S GUIDE: Now that you're both officially desirable bachelors, what advice would you have for a guy in today's busy world to be accessible, available, and attractive to women?

> **BERKLEY:** Do what you love to do and try to make a difference in life—whether in local circles or the world at large. That approach is the best way to meet good people and attract them. You're not really going to achieve that by hitting the bars and nightclubs.

WILLENSON: A sense of balance in life is very important. For the past 10 years, I have been almost singularly focused on establishing Camp Heartland as the international leader in pediatric-HIV camping and care. On top of that, I am serving as the producer for an upcoming feature film, *Hunting Season*. This has not left me with a great deal of time to focus on my personal life.

I have learned, however, that a sense of balance is very healthy and important. Why achieve great things if you have no one to enjoy your accomplishments with? Lately, I have committed myself to focusing more attention on my personal life. Ultimately, I want a family and don't want life to pass me by.

To be "attractive" to women, I try to be caring, attentive, and maintain a sense of humor. Physically, I work out on a daily basis and I enjoy being in good shape.

MAN'S GUIDE: What are the best traits you see among your male friends and peers in terms of hitting it off with the ladies?

BERKLEY: Humor, humility, honesty.

WILLENSON: My peers and friends who have been successful with women have been attentive, caring, and fun. In addition, they have communicated well with the women they are with—be they girlfriends or wives.

MAN'S GUIDE: Dr. Berkley, you had earlier hinted at the superficiality that so many people exhibit in terms of their dating activities and relationships. Are these three Hs you cite—humor, humility, and honesty—the traits people look at when they "grow up" but ignore through much of their early dating life?

BERKLEY: I think substantive people look at that stuff. That's really the difference between people of substance and people who don't even try to have substance. We're in an environment of sound bites and flash-in-the-pan fame—and you know, people are impressed with that stuff. But it's not what's [truly] impressive. What *is* impressive is being a good person and making the world a better place. And that could be to try to save the world from AIDS, or it could be raising really good kids and making sure they have the right moral values. People lose sight of that stuff.

MAN'S GUIDE: Where do you guys fall when it comes to wanting freedom versus commitment?

BERKLEY: On the one hand, I love my single life. I'm able to juggle my work and play with impunity. I meet fascinating women. The truth be told, though, I would love to share all of the wonderful things in my life with the right person.

WILLENSON: I am an extremely independent person. Being a bachelor has allowed me to focus the time and attention on projects that are very important to me.

Yet as I've reached the 30 milestone, I am becoming more focused on getting married and starting a family. As a result, I may not be as focused on my extracurricular activities, such as the feature-film project. On the other hand, I will have someone to enjoy my life with.

MAN'S GUIDE: Anyone have any last words of wisdom?

BERKLEY: Well, I don't know if it's wisdom, but I'll tell you what my personal motto in life is: Live like you're going to die tomorrow; learn like you're going to live forever.

You want to keep living and learning and growing because when your brain stops working, that's it. Game over.

QUICKIES

MAKE YOUR VOICE HEARD

When you ask for a raise or flirt with a waitress, you want to sound as smooth and persuasive as James Earl Jones. But what if your voice squeaks like R2D2's? Then you need to make your voice more powerful. To do that, try these exercises from Anna Bernstein, owner of Voice Success, a voice-coaching company in New York City.

The Siren: In private, hum back and forth between the bottom and top of your vocal range, like a siren. Repeat the cycle 10 times, once or twice a day. This will help you vary your pitch when speaking, making your voice sound more interesting and emphatic.

The Hum: To keep your voice from cracking unexpectedly during a presentation, warm up by humming a few bars of a song. Make sure you stop before you enter the conference room. Especially if you're humming 'N Sync.

The Tongue Flip: If you mumble or constantly trip up on words, it's usually a sign that your tongue is getting jumbled up with your lips and teeth when you talk. Improve your enunciation with this exercise: Place the tip of your tongue in front of your upper lip. Flick your tongue to the inside of your top teeth and back. Do this as fast as you can for a few minutes each day. (Your girlfriend will thank you.)

A HEALTH BENEFIT OF BEING FAT?

So you've put on a few pounds these past few years. Here's reason to celebrate anyway: New research from Sweden suggests that a wider belly may actually provide protection from testicular cancer, the most common cancer in men younger than age 35.

The study, conducted at the Karolinska Institute in Sweden, used data collected on 500,000 Norwegians over 26 years. Researchers compared the subjects' Body Mass Index (a measure of their build), height, and age to the incidence of testicular cancer over the course of the study. Their findings showed that slender guys taller than six feet were 34 percent more likely to develop testicular cancer than were their shorter, stockier counterparts.

"Being overweight or obese actually appeared to be associated with a decreased risk for testicular cancer," says study leader Olof Akre, M.D. Tall individuals are thought to have increased exposure to growth hormone, while obese men produce less testosterone, Dr. Akre explains. Both hormones are believed to play a role in the growth of tumors.

Though this news may give the George Costanzas of the world a reason to smirk, it's no excuse for a second slice of cheesecake. "Testicular cancer is a rare disease that generally strikes young men," says Akre. Most guys—especially those in middle age—should be more worried about heart disease and prostate cancer.

LEK ME BABY

Lekking refers to male animals convening to make silly displays as they compete for females. (Think peacock.) Two University of Liverpool professors spent 4 months observing guys flaunting their cell phones in a pub and concluded that lekking is what they do.

Unless you have a particularly snazzy cell phone, don't bother. As wireless prices have plummeted and the phones have become ubiquitous, "I would expect them to have less value as a display item," says one of the researchers, Robin Dunbar.

If you're determined to strut your stuff, traditional examples of conspicuous consumption such as a gold Rolex or a Versace suit will still assure you a night of heavy lekking.

YOUR HAIR, YOUR SELF

The Supreme Court didn't cost Al Gore the presidency—his hairdresser did. At least according to John Walter and his sister Catherine, who are makers and purveyors of New York City's True Mirrors—mirrors that offer an accurate self-assessment by reflecting a nonmirror image of the viewer. When you look into the mirror, you see yourself as others see you. Men who part their hair on the right—as Gore does—are perceived as right-brain men, characterized by such feminine traits as sensitivity.

Men who part their hair on the left—think George W. Bush—draw attention to such traditionally masculine left-brain qualities as forcefulness. The Walters point out that Americans have elected only three men with right parts—Buchanan, Harding, and Reagan.

The best bet, says John Walter, is to have no part at all, because "you can pretty much be what you choose to be."

ASK THE SEX DOC

Q: *I have a skinny neck.* **What can I do to make it look bigger?**
—J. K., DELRAY BEACH, FLORIDA

A: Skinny ties may have worked in 1984, but they do nothing for your neck. Woven ties tied in a Windsor knot look thicker, which will make your neck look more substantial. Wear them with a spread-collar shirt rather than a point-collar to create the illusion of a meatier neck.

Q: *I ran out of shaving cream, so I had to use soap to shave. I actually got a better shave.* **Is it okay to shave with soap every day?**
—R. D., PUTNEY, VERMONT

A: Absolutely. Shaving cream is just soap that's processed into a foamier form, so one really works as well as the other. You'll produce the best results with one of the rich, creamy brands your wife uses, such as Aveeno or Dove. They have moisturizers, so they won't dry your skin. Leave the deodorant soaps for other body parts. Zest might make your armpits tingle, but it's much too harsh for your face.

Q: *What happens when male celebrities get acne?* **How do they get rid of it fast?**
—L. M., WILMINGTON, NORTH CAROLINA

A: Men break out more than women because they pay less attention to their skin, says Mally Roncal, a New York makeup artist who has toiled over the tender flesh of Dylan McDermott, Kyle MacLachlan, and Michael Stipe. She tells her men to use Mario Badescu Drying Lotion ($17, www.mariobadescu.com) every night to dry pimples.

During the day, keep the area clean with an oil-free cloth. (Roncal prefers Bioré Facial Cleansing Cloths, $5.50 for 34 cloths, available at any drugstore.) "This is especially important if you sweat a lot during the day," says Roncal. "Keep them in your gym bag." To take the red out of a sore pimple, use a drop of Visine directly on the skin. Roncal notes that this quick fix lasts only about an hour (or, to put it in Hollywood terms, roughly the length of Jared Leto's film career).

Q: *I just found a product called Semenex that's advertised on the web. It's supposed to improve the flavor of your ejaculate. **What do you guys think?***
—G. M., KEARNEY, NEBRASKA

A: This looks to us like one of those cases where something that sounds too good to be true probably is. The manufacturers of Semenex claim that their product will make semen taste better by bombarding your system with natural concentrations of all the foods that can reportedly do the job on their own—things like pineapple juice, celery, and strawberries.

The problem with the supplement—assuming it works—is that it would mask the flavor of your semen instead of sweetening it. Unless you change your diet, whatever is causing your semen to taste bitter remains in your system. Making an effort to actually eat more fruit will not only help you eat less meat and salty foods, it will also help remove toxins from your system, which may sweeten your taste.

Plus, consider how much fresh fruit you could buy for a single $2 dose of Semenex.

The Sex Doc is a fictional character. The actual advice was provided by a variety of medical doctors and other qualified experts.

3

PROMOTE
PERPETUAL
PASSION

 We're not going to lie to you. You may never recapture the days when you and your first love stayed naked all day long and had sex until you were both sore. Back then, passion ruled your universe. Now, we bet, it's been dethroned by more practical concerns.

What the hell happened?

We can't go into all the details (mothers-in-law, career changes, mortgage payments, kids, mothers-in-law . . .), but we will tell you this: Though glory days may be gone, there's still plenty of majesty left in your kingdom.

We've talked with a lot of couples over the years—of all ages—and you'd be amazed by the number that say the sex is still great. The difference: When you're young and in love, great sex comes naturally. Without the "young" part, you simply have to make a more noble effort. Don't worry, it's easy. These next pages provide the tools to make passion reign supreme again.

Sexual Slipups

Some of us are born screwups, but the last place you want to screw up is, well, when you're screwing. Here are 10 sexual miscues virtually guaranteed to make sleep the only thing happening between your sheets. Obligatory reminder: These are don'ts.

① **Play beat the clock.** On your mark, get set, wham-bam-thank-you-ma'am. Treat sex as a sprint, not a distance race. One sure way to let your lover know she's on the clock: Check your watch several times during foreplay. In fact, just wearing a watch is a good indicator.

② **Take it oh-so-seriously.** The "it's my job to make my partner come" attitude guarantees neither one of you will have a good time. Furrow your brow, frown a lot, and check the sex manual under the pillow to make sure you are following the instructions precisely.

③ **Be selfish.** Make sure you climax first, then "service" her after. If at all. This will go over really big. In fact, use this technique often enough and the whole relationship may be over.

④ **Welcome uninvited kids.** Children who pop into your room whenever they want to are the best guarantee that you'll never have to worry about having any more kids. It's just a shame there's absolutely nothing you can do about it. (Unless, of course, you count locks. Or hotels. Or sleep-overs. Or grandparents.)

⑤ **Make scents.** Just before you get into bed, smoke a cigar, a pipe, and a cigarette. That should be preceded by garlic-smothered pizza. (Don't brush your teeth.) Which all should be preceded by a sweaty tennis match—hold the shower. The combined odor should leave no doubt that you have no respect for her—or yourself.

6 **Bring your anger to bed.** In the 1989 film *The War of the Roses*, an estranged wife, played by Kathleen Turner, asks an attorney, portrayed by Danny DeVito: "Have you ever made angry love?" He replies, "Is there any other way?" Not that a divorce lawyer would relish. So if you want to turn a hot woman frigid, bring up past offenses as part of foreplay. Better yet, suppress your anger and let it out in sarcastic jabs.

7 **Bring stress to bed.** You missed the train. You lost the account. You spilled soy sauce on your silk tie. The annual budget is due tomorrow. You're losing your hair, gaining too much weight, and aging before your very eyes. Now go ahead—try to get it up (we won't hold our breath). Then, make sure to blame her for your impotence.

8 **Sidestep seduction.** She lights some candles. Blow them out and turn the lights up. She tells you all about her day. Cut her off. Going out to dinner? Throw on your favorite grungy T and some grass-stained jeans. And above all, resist the urge to swap your holey tighty-whiteys for those silk boxers stuffed in the bottom of your drawer.

9 **Repeat the same position.** Choose your favorite sex position and stick with it. During foreplay, touch her in the same places and in the same way every time. If she asks to try something new, remind her you're a creature of habit. She'll wish she had listened to Sister Mary Catherine and was wearing one.

10 **Ignore her signals.** If she moans or groans at any point during your lovemaking, stop whatever you're doing and rub her somewhere else. If she says "That feels good" or "Oh, yes!" do whatever it is you're doing twice as fast. And never ask her if she likes something. Just do what *you* like and assume that she enjoys it, too.

MUST READS

Same Woman, Better Sex

She's a great catch. Smart, funny, gorgeous. The kids love her and she's a hell of a Trivial Pursuit partner. She'd be the perfect woman in every way . . . if only she'd do that thing with her tongue you saw in Wild Orchid. *There's hope. Here, Zachary Veilleux explains how to teach a great girl a few new tricks.*

We wish every woman treated sex as if it were a Bruce Willis movie—nonstop action, lots of screams, 20 explosions per minute. If you feel the same way, maybe it's time you traded in your silent partner for someone a bit more adventurous. Someone who knows enough sex tricks to write her own HBO series. Follow our advice and you won't have to look far. She's sleeping next to you. Yeah, that's right, the very same woman in the long flannel nightgown, who nodded off over *Martha Stewart Living* at 8:30. Well, it's time for a wake-up call.

⊙ Problem: She initiates sex as often as the Cubs make the World Series.
While one survey showed that nearly two-thirds of women say they initiate sex at least sometimes, the bad news is that she counts occasional hair-flipping as initiation. At least once every few weeks, it would be nice to have our shirts torn apart by someone other than the dry cleaner.

Solution: Buy her new shoes.

It works two ways. One, you're playing into her idea of foreplay: Doing something terribly nice and out of the ordinary makes her want you more. And, even more important, it gives you the chance to work all of those sensitive nerve endings in her feet. When you check her for fit, linger around the tips of her toes. Don't be surprised if she kicks off her shoes as soon as you get home.

⊙ Problem: She hides her body under sheets, pillows, and you.
You've spent your life imagining your body next to airbrushed frauleins from beer commercials. She's spent the same time comparing herself with them. If she doesn't like to reveal flesh, it's probably because she's not comfortable showing it off to you.

Solution: Stop telling her how much you love her legs.

Women are weird this way. "If you say something nice about her breasts, she'll just wonder why you don't like her butt," says Pamela Regan, Ph.D., a psychologist at California State University in Los Angeles. Go for general compliments. Tell her, "Your body is incredible."

● **Problem: Your bedroom sounds like high school detention—silence, with maybe a few giggles.**

Men love it when women moan, scream, and pant. It makes it sound—to the flight attendants, anyway—as if we know what we're doing.

Solution: Create chaos.

If she's quiet, it's probably because she's afraid of waking the pilots. So create background noise to make her feel relaxed—run the dishwasher, have sex in the shower, drop a CD. You can even sing a little: When you're giving her oral sex, hum along. The low vibrations from your vocal cords will feel incredible to her. Press firmly with your lips; that's where you'll generate the most vibration.

perfect figures

IT'S A MAGIC NUMBER.

Percentage of American adults who rate their sex life A or A-plus:
69

● **Problem: She's squeamish about giving you oral sex.**

Maybe she's shy, maybe she doesn't know what you like, maybe she equates oral sex with an unpleasant circus trick.

Solution: Turn her hands into a bumper.

Lou Paget, author of *How to Give Her Absolute Pleasure* and *The Big O*, gives seminars on proper oral-sex technique. So she's a hero in our book, especially after she shared this tip for mouth-to-south resuscitation. When your partner starts giving you oral sex, take her hands off your thighs and hold them with yours (she'll like that). Then guide her hands to your penis so they form a tube around it. As her mouth goes up and down, rotate her hands clockwise and counterclockwise. The bonus for you: Different tactile sensations make it feel even better than straight oral sex. The bonus for her: Smooth sailing will boost her confidence. Her hands will act as a comfortable bumper between the 3 inches of her mouth and the 5 inches (or more) of your penis.

● **Problem: She won't lay a hand on you.**

There's no reason why foreplay has to be limited to kissing, unhooking straps, and kicking the dog out of the room.

Solution: Tell her your neck hurts.

Sex without fondling is more of a drag race than a pleasure trip: No warmup and you'll be lucky if it lasts 3.2 seconds. Your goal is to have her take a few laps around your body, with several important pit stops. Start by complaining of a stiff neck. After she helps out, offer to do hers. Switch body parts back and forth. When she starts reaching your lower half, take her hands and have her position one hand vertically, the other horizontally—palm to palm. She'll then lower these palms of pleasure over your penis. When she strokes you, your penis will slide up between her fingers. Use a little Astroglide and she'll have you bleating out of her hand.

"Turn Me Loose!"

WHAT TURNED FIVE WALLFLOWERS INTO WILD WOMEN

"I dated a guy who absolutely refused to orgasm unless I did. At first, his high expectations were annoying as hell. But eventually he raised my expectations, and now I think, 'There's no way I'm not coming during sex.' Frankly, that makes it better for the man, too."
—Amanda, 27

"I like giving oral sex, but I always avoided touching the satchel—I was afraid I'd do something wrong or hurt the guy. But the first time I was with my husband, he stopped everything and gave me this amazing testicle demonstration—showing me all the different ways you can play with them, stroke them, tickle them. . . . It was very hands-on and hugely enlightening."
—Andrea, 29

"We were in bed, and he said two words: 'You're beautiful.' All of a sudden I was a super sex goddess."
—Lois, 28

"Unlike other men I've been with, my husband likes to make love at odd times of the day—like 2:00 on a Tuesday afternoon, or in the middle of the night, or right before dinner. And that sort of taught me that sex wasn't this afterthought, it was an activity in itself—something you could make a date to do all by itself, and definitely not something to be hidden under a pile of blankets."
—Selma, 31

"His name was Vincent, but it should have been Eric Clapton, because he had that crazy slow-hand thing working. Once he taught me how to hold off my orgasm, I became addicted to this self-denying activity. Rather than racing to the finish, I started to relax and enjoy the journey. And there's so much that goes on before your orgasm! I'm a lot more relaxed and fun now."
—Ondine, 34

◑ Problem: The frequency of her orgasms roughly coincides with congressional elections.

Her orgasms don't just make her feel good; they're an undeniable marker of your success as a sex machine. The fewer she has, the wimpier you feel.

Solution: Distract her.

The top cause of orgasmic difficulty in women is that they're thinking about it too much, says Mark Elliott, Ph.D., a sex therapist. If you can keep her mind on other things, you increase the chances that her quakes will be picked up by the geology department at the local U. Try "69," kiss her passionately while having intercourse, encourage her to tell you about her fantasies as she gets more and more aroused—anything to keep her from focusing on why she's not having an orgasm. If that fails, tell her about this position: While she's on top, she should push her left leg forward so it slides slightly toward your head (her knees stay bent) and gently slide her right leg toward your feet. Every few thrusts, she should alternate positions. The pelvic pressure this position creates—and the rotation around your penis—is pretty damn orgasmic. If she asks where you heard about it, do what we do: Say you read about it.

◑ Problem: She won't experiment.

For many women, it boils down to this: She thinks that if she tries fancy techniques, you'll think she's a slut.

Solution: Give her a squeaky-clean source of dirty ideas (and cheesecake recipes).

Buy her a subscription to *Redbook*—surprisingly, by our count, an average issue has more information about sex technique than other women's magazines. Do whatever you want to get it in your house: Tell her you found it on the train, or in the men's-room stall. It won't be long before she's searching for "35 New Places to Touch a Man."

◑ Problem: You want her to know more about your outrageous sexual fantasies than the video-rental clerk does.

Solution: Gear down.

Remember back when you were first dating? You didn't let her see all your strange quirks and unpleasant habits at once. First you told her about your preference for tube socks, and later—much later—you unveiled your lifelong dream of becoming an igloo architect. To encourage a shy woman to buy into your sexual fantasies, introduce props or role-playing in small doses. In other words, you have to ask her to put her hair in a ponytail and chew bubble gum well before you break out the pom-poms.

How to Get More Sex

When it comes to sex, some men know that turning a woman on is about more than just finding the right nerve endings. It's about connecting with her brain before you connect with any of her other parts. In this excerpt from Command Respect *(Rodale, 1998), Perry Garfinkel, Brian Kaufman, and the editors of* Men's Health *Books tell you the best ways to stimulate a woman with your tongue.*

What's a four-letter word for intercourse that ends in *k*?

Wrong.

It's T-A-L-K. Talk about yourself, talk about your real and true self. Not the I-did-this, I-own-that, I-know-such-and-such and what's-his-name monologue some men deliver. That's a sure turn off, a bellwether of disrespect.

"The real turn-on that women desperately crave is an intensely private revelation of feelings from a man—a portal into his inner soul," says Robert C. Kolodny, M.D., medical director and chairman of the nonprofit Behavioral Medicine Institute in New Canaan, Connecticut, and co-author with William Masters and Virginia Johnson of *Heterosexuality*. "The starting point of respectful sex between consenting adults is the presentation of yourself in an honest and forthright way."

And then there's the kind of foreplay that involves the ears. Not the whisper-in-her-ear-and-she'll-follow-you-anywhere variety. But rather listening—*really listening*—to what a woman is saying. Not so that you can come up with some clever repartee in response, but in order to hear what her heart and soul are trying to tell you.

"The sexiest thing you can do is really pay attention when she's talking," says Bonnie Jacobson, Ph.D., director of the New York Institute for Psychological Change and author of *If Only You Would Listen*.

If there were more of this sort of respectful sexual foreplay, there would be a lot more men and women walking around the streets with that telltale morning-after glow.

Be Honest

The key to a respectful attitude toward making love to a woman begins way before intercourse. As with every other human relationship, it has to do with honoring the wishes and desires of your mate. "It's about treating others as you would like to be treated," explains Dr. Kolodny.

That starts with honesty. When you meet a woman, do you tell her you're not involved with someone when you really are? Do you say you want to be in her life when you really mean you just want to be in her bed? Do you say you've made love to only five women in your life when the truth is you're challenging Wilt Chamberlain's record (and we don't mean most points scored in a basketball game)? Do you whisper in her ear "I love you" when you mean "I lust you"? The next morning do you say "I'll call you later" when you mean "I'll call you when Elvis resurfaces"?

These are among the most common lies men tell women, according to *Sexual Awareness* co-author Barry McCarthy, Ph.D., a psychologist at the Washington Psychological Center who teaches a course in human sexual behavior at American University in Washington, D.C.

"Making promises you don't intend to keep is disrespectful," says Dr. McCarthy. "Don't oversell how much intimacy you want to have just to score."

Most women see right through that. Eventually, it catches up to you when she—and every girlfriend she talks to—catches on.

Along with honesty come integrity, trustworthiness, reliability, and the other traits that distinguish the well-respected man. Then there's having the appropriate attitude. Too often men approach sex as something they "get." As in "getting laid," or "Did you get any last night?" This does not bode well for healthy and respectful give-and-take sexual involvement. It implies that women are there for your pleasure.

SEX TRENDS

SECRETS OF A LONG-TERM MARRIAGE

Want your marriage to last? Then don't model it after your favorite movie, says Ted Huston, Ph.D., a professor of psychology at the University of Texas in Austin. Huston and his colleagues at the school came to this conclusion after following 156 couples over 14 years of marriage. His biggest finding? People in more mundane, leisurely courtships generally aren't entertaining wild fantasies about one another, and they're more likely to have an accurate and honest view of their partner. So they're not so disappointed later on, once the novelty wears off. Couples that move into a relationship quickly, in contrast, often have expectations that things are going to stay the same once they're married. They don't really know each other as well as they imagine, and they're more likely to eventually become disappointed in each other.

"Sex is a shared experience," Dr. Jacobson says. "It turns out that the more you give of yourself, the more you'll get in return."

Regardless of your current marital status, there are basically three stages to the lovemaking ritual: before, during, and after. What follows are guidelines for each stage that will make sure you always show your mate the highest respect.

Before Sex

So they want to see into our inner soul, do they? Well, some men take that idea to the extreme, dumping all their grief and vulnerability on an unsuspecting woman. If that's your version of sharing, go tell your shrink. "You don't want to dump," Dr. Jacobson says. "You want to connect." The way to connect is to "build a bridge," she notes. If you want to talk about serious subjects—like losing a close friend—start by asking her if she has ever suffered any losses. Let her reveal some of hers. Then say, "Well, then you probably can relate to what I'm going through." Then share your grief with her.

If you've done this in a sensitive and sincere manner, believe it or not, you've just had great foreplay. Because great sex starts with great foreplay, and great foreplay starts with touching a woman—that is, touching her emotionally. Here are other ways to touch her.

perfect figures

NOT COUNTING THE ONES
WHO DIDN'T PLAN TO,
BUT DO ANYWAY.

Percentage of college
students who plan to live
with their parents
after graduation:
56

● ● ● ● ● ● ● ● ● ●

● **Listen empathetically.**

There's no way to con a woman into thinking you are listening to her when you're actually listening to the hockey game on the radio. "Women have a very sensitive barometer, and they'll know you're only pretending to listen," says Rosalyn Meadow, Ph.D., a Phoenix-based sex therapist and author of *Good Girls Don't Eat Dessert.*

The giveaway is that you have a different look on your face; there's a different level of attentiveness in your eyes. Listening empathetically involves trying to understand the feelings behind what she's saying. "Enter her world," says Dr. Meadow. "Listen in an uncritical, nonjudgmental manner." Maintain eye contact. Resist the man's natural urge to jump in and solve her problems. If she wanted a problem-solver, she would have called her lawyer.

◉ Plan unplanned time.

This may be truer for married or committed men, but single men should take note, too. Allow unscheduled time and space in which "nothing has to happen," suggests Dr. Jacobson. "That's where real contact is made." That's when a woman knows you want to be with her for who she is, not for how good she looks on your arm at the opera, or for what you have in mind for after the fat lady sings.

◉ Watch for love signals.

Most men are oblivious to women's sexual overtures, says biologist Timothy Perper, Ph.D., a Philadelphia-based sex researcher and author of *Sex Signals*. In his research, he found that women initiate courtship gestures more than two-thirds of the time. At a social gathering, women will approach, talk, turn toward a man, and—most important—make physical contact in a subtle manner that goes right over men's heads. A light touch on the hand or elbow can be the female equivalent of a neon sign shouting, "Make love to me." It would show a woman great respect to let her do what comes naturally—initiate—rather than force yourself on her. And if she does not return your gestures—if she looks away, if she doesn't lean toward you—these are sure signs she's not into it, Dr. Perper says. The respectful thing to do is back off and let it go. Ironically, that sign of respect may win you points at another time.

◉ Mean what you say.

"It has to come naturally, from the heart," says Dr. Meadow. "If it's contrived or part of a strategy, it will come off falsely." And lying is no way to show respect. We suggest you read all this advice and file it in your subconscious, where it will take seed and later blossom organically as a many-petaled flower of love.

During Sex

You may think the sexual revolution began in the Summer of Love and ended in the Era of AIDS. But women are redefining their sexual needs in a worldwide gender revolution that's still going on in every one of 32 countries surveyed by Robert Francoeur, Ph.D., professor of biology and sexuality at Fairleigh Dickinson University

Turns out there's no reason to hide your dirty videos under your floor mats. She may enjoy watching them just as much as you do, according to one Australian study. Researchers found that men and women had similar physiological responses to watching the videos, with one notable exception: When women watched the action, they secreted even more adrenaline than men did.

in Madison, New Jersey, and author of *The International Encyclopedia of Sexuality*.

The new buzzword is "outercourse," he says. "Women are oriented toward the whole body, not just the genitals," he says. "They're redefining sex in terms of ecstasy. They want it to include a sense of transcendence." Talk about performance pressure. Now we have to worry about satisfying women spiritually as well as sexually. We have to make respectful love that makes her scream, "Oo-o-oo . . ." and then chant, "Oo-o-o-ommmm. . . ."

This, too, is doable. Here's how.

● Have the condom conversation.

In these times, unless you've been monogamous with the same person since the 1970s, contracting a sexually transmitted disease is not a remote possibility. It may be one of the most awkward moments in the dance of sex, but to show the highest respect to a first-time lover, you have to raise the question of protection. The most honest approach is the most forthright, says Dr. Perper. "Do you mind if I wear a condom?"

If you suggest it before she does, that is a signal that you respect her and you value both your lives. AIDS is a deadly disease, and this is no time to pretend otherwise. The where and when are up to you.

However, Dr. Perper suggests not leaving it to the moment before intercourse. That will deflate the moment and, quite possibly, your erection.

● Let her be the expert.

Guess what. She knows what she likes better than you do. Rather than forge ahead caveman-style, let her take charge, suggests Dr. McCarthy. If she doesn't offer, ask. Or try something and ask, "Do you like this?"

● Check out her breathing.

Women start breathing faster and deeper and louder when they get aroused. Be attentive to these and other signs that she's having a good time. "Be attuned to the nuances of your partner's body," Dr. Kolodny says. The nonverbal cues, like heavy breathing, the slight sweat of her skin, and that musky perfume that exudes from between her legs—Dr. Francoeur calls the scent of a sexually aroused woman vaginal pheromones—are among the signs that you are demonstrating how much you respect her body.

● Make variety the spice of your sex life.

Send the missionary position on a retreat. Try it sideways, from the back, and other new variations on the age-old theme. Also, if the bed is your sole sexual arena, move the action to the living room or the kitchen or the garage. Wear your cowboy boots to bed. "The point is that even the most exciting endeavor can become boring," Dr. Perper says. Try something new; then in 6 months, when hanging from the chandelier becomes boring, go back to Position One.

● **Talk dirty—with respect.**
First, a warning. One style of talking dirty is using the most taboo of profane words, commands, and references to body parts that would make Andrew Dice Clay blush. The other is the more gentlemanly play-by-play between consenting adults in which each thought and gesture is shared out loud—to the excitement of all involved. Some women love either style. Some, to put it mildly, don't. Dr. Perper suggests either letting her initiate the love talk or slowly introducing it yourself with mild obscenities like, "What a beautiful (fill in your favorite female body part here) you have." If she recoils, cease and desist, advises Dr. Perper.

> **"** It has been wisely said that we cannot really love anybody at whom we never laugh. **"**
>
> —Agnes Repplier

● **Invent your own language of love.**
One of the problems with sex communication is that "proper words seem cold, and slang words seem hostile," says Dr. McCarthy. His alternative: Develop your own unique private sexual language. Make up vocabulary words that don't even make sense, Lewis Carroll-esque nouns referring to body parts or verbs for things you want to do to each other. "This is one way to personalize and individualize the lovemaking," says Dr. McCarthy, and to demonstrate to your lover the exclusivity of your relationship.

● **Avoid spectatoring.**
That's a term used by Georgia Witkin, Ph.D., director of the Stress Program at Mt. Sinai Hospital in Manhattan and author of *The Male Stress Syndrome*. It's a habit men have of checking out their own performance while they're still performing. It's like watching yourself through a camcorder placed on the ceiling. "Men have been performing all day at work," she says. "It's natural to keep doing it right into the bedroom." But it's damaging and impedes sexual spontaneity. Anyway, it pays more respect to your sex partner to let go of self-consciousness and focus on *her* body.

● **Get consensus.**
Now you're both involved in active sex play, but you want her to be in another position. Commanding her to turn over or move over may come off as too con-

trolling to some women. Dr. Perper offers this variation: Gently push her body where you'd like it to be. If that doesn't work, say, "Do you mind if I move you over here?" This wording is key. "I've known a number of women who have explicitly described being turned on by that subtle demonstration of control and at the same time respect for and acceptance of her femininity," he says.

● **Put off the pouting.**

That sad look on your face, the Ringo eyes, and those curled lips when she says, "Not tonight" or "Not there" are subtle forms of coercion that have no sex appeal, Dr. McCarthy says. They may get you what you want that moment, but they will diminish your chances of getting what you want again. "You'll win the battle but lose the war," he notes, because she'll feel manipulated, and manipulation is disrespectful.

After Sex

For some men, staying connected after sex is not the problem; it's staying awake. If that's you, catch some Zzzs earlier in the day or get your beauty rest the night before. How you show love and respect after you make love is the sign of a truly concerned lover. So wake up and pay attention.

● **Make suggestions later, not sooner.**

The goal is mutually satisfying sex. If she's not doing it in a manner that you enjoy, it's okay to tell her. When and how are the key issues. "It's better to not talk about it right after or during the interaction," advises Dr. Kolodny. "It sounds like you're a music critic and you're writing a review of the performance. That's one of the fastest ways to get a woman riled up."

Bring up technique at a time and place that's detached from that moment. Preface your suggestion this way: "I'm very nervous about bringing this up because it could sound like criticism, but I care about you so much that I want our sexual relationship to be the best it can be."

● **Clean up later.**

This is clearly not the sole domain of men, but some men who are a little too obsessive about cleanliness will jump out of bed and run to the bathroom to sponge themselves off right after

hot TIP!

As if you needed one, here's another reason to sink your wife's inheritance in the stock market: Psychologists at the State University of New York at Stony Brook found that couples who engaged in high-risk activities reported that they felt more passionate than couples who didn't. Important point: Buy low, sell high.

orgasm. "It definitely takes the glow off the moment," says OnHealth sex advisor Louanne Weston. "It makes a woman think her bodily fluids revolt you." If they do, discreetly bring a little hand towel to bedside and wipe off.

◉ Cuddle.

We all know women love to cuddle after great (or even not-so-great) sex. Why? It may be because they are more used to being cuddled as little girls, suggests Dr. Weston. It doesn't necessarily mean that they want to smother you or that they need attention all the time. If you jump up and grab the remote control right after sex, you're sending the message that your lover was interesting only as long as she was giving you pleasure.

"Women want a sense of continuity," Dr. Weston says. If cuddling feels too claustrophobic, or if it makes you sweat, hold her hand. The main thing is for you to stay connected in a tactile way.

perfect figures

123 4567890
1234567890

POLITICIANS EXCLUDED FROM SURVEY.

Percentage of Americans who believe in one true love:
74

· · · · · · · · · ·

◉ Brush your teeth.

If you're a normal human being, your breath may not be worthy of being bottled and sold as perfume. If you're planning to kiss your lover in the morning or engage in face-to-face pillow talk, sneak out of bed, tiptoe to the bathroom, and brush those pearly whites. "Almost every woman in the world would consider that a sign of respect," says Dr. Weston. And it might encourage her to do the same.

THE FUNNY PAGE

"For God's sake, Edith, I'm trying to read the paper!"

HELP ONLINE

TURN YOUR BEDROOM INTO A TOY ROOM

Put the "play" into your foreplay with sex toys you can buy without ever leaving the comfort of your own keyboard. Choose from all sorts of items ranging from costumes and fur-lined shackles to leather lingerie or vibrators. But buyer beware. Just as some adult shops can be on the seamy side, so it is with some Internet merchants. If you decide to buy online, look for a company that offers these consumer-friendly policies: (1) a money-back guarantee, (2) a willingness to replace defective products without sending you to the original manufacturer, (3) a privacy policy that includes sending its products in plain, unidentifiable wrapping, and (4) a policy to never sell or rent your name to other companies.

Here are a few cybershops we checked out that fit the bill:

www.babeland.com

Toys in Babeland is a sex toy store run by women striving to celebrate sexual vitality. (We're all for a celebration.) Don't let the fact that it's run by women scare you off. There are plenty of toys for boys, plus lubes, an erotic massage video, and much more.

www.xandria.com

Not sure what a "bullet" is? Or where it goes? Check out this site's sex toy glossary to find out. Xandria's been in business 25 years and also boasts an impressive selection of toys for erotic play. Browse its large array of condoms designed to enhance pleasure for both of you. Or surprise her with a leather or snakeskin jock. For her, there are nipple toys, body jewelry, and items we can't mention here.

www.goodvibes.com

Good Vibrations has been known as a reputable adult shop since 1977. On its site you'll find do-it-yourself toys and creams for increased self-pleasure, plus finger paints, edible undies, sex board games, and much, much more. Just for kicks, visit the site's Antique Vibrator Museum to see what used to get great-grandma off. (Not *your* great-grandma, of course.)

www.adameve.com

With over 30 years' experience in the adult-products biz, Adam & Eve is the nation's leader in adult mail order with more than four million customers. They sell hard-to-find sex novelties, including a life-size blow-up doll and an edible dusting powder that comes complete with its own feather brush. Please note that Adam & Eve *does* sell its customers' names to other companies, but you can call their toll-free number to request that your name not be sold.

www.focusint.com

Part of the Sinclair Intimacy Institute, this site offers more than 60 adult sex education videos (They must know that sex ed is our favorite subject). On its companion site, www.intimacyinstitute.com, you'll find a vast array of all things slippery, not to mention a library of sex games, books, and romantic music to choose from.

www.mypleasure.com

Aimed at the sophisticated customer, this site offers high-quality sensual products as well as articles, education, and advice from sex experts. For the toys, we recommend you check out the "El Matador" and the site's section called "Remote Control Fun." The first is a specially-designed cock ring to enhance your pleasure. As for the remote control items . . . let's just say you'll be able to get her motor running with the push of a button, anywhere, anytime.

MAN'S GUIDE INTERVIEW

More Fun Than the Fridge: Why Sex Toys Are the Best Household Appliances

An Interview with Carol Queen and Joyce Solano

These days, some marriages don't last as long as the blenders the bride got at her shower. But maybe they would if couples could register for sex toys instead. Carol Queen, Ed.D., and Joyce Solano of Good Vibrations, a San Francisco sex-toy shop and online retailer, gave us practical advice on using toys to keep your sex life permanently playful. They even told us about one fun-filled gadget that magically runs for 20 years.

Want to bring that kind of staying power to your relationship? Read on.

MAN'S GUIDE: Some men find sex toys threatening. What would you tell them to help them become more comfortable?

QUEEN: First, we call them toys for a reason: They're playthings. Their focus is to increase the kinds of sensuality that you, or you and a partner, can experience.

They used to be called marital aids. In the first place, you do not have to be married, and you do not need to use one just because you need help sexually. The whole notion that sex toys fix something that's wrong, I think, comes from that terminology; and I think that's one of the things that men are reading when they are concerned about toys.

I would really encourage men to think of toys as their allies in pleasure.

SOLANO: My experience is that a lot of men say, "This place [the Good Vibrations store] is for women. What do you have that *I* can use?" I think it's about realizing that we are really all made out of the same tissue and that what feels really good for a lot of women is also going to be adaptable to men.

MAN'S GUIDE: How do you get that message out there?

QUEEN: For a long time, besides working in the store, my primary job in the company was as director of continuing education. My responsibility was to help train the staff to talk to people knowledgeably and comfortably about these issues. One of the things that's relevant to men and toys is, again, getting back to the idea of: Is it supposed to fix something that's broken? And do they have a limited idea about what sexual pleasure can be?

Prior to Viagra, many men came to shop for themselves at the store specifically to "get fixed." They were often a little older. They were not having erections reliably anymore. And they wanted to get a pump or cock ring, something that they had heard about either from friends or in an article or from a doctor. Which is all well and good; although we really wanted to emphasize for those men: If you haven't seen a doctor about your erectile issues, you must. You can't self-medicate with a cock ring. There may be things going on that you can be helped with, that you *should* be helped with, that a ring or a pump might even affect negatively and make your health worse.

> **"**It is an extra dividend when you like the girl you've fallen in love with. **"**
>
> —Clark Gable

Another thing was the notion that "I need an erection so I can have sex." They forget that there is infinitely more to sex than penetration, than erection. Men and women both have fundamentally the same tissue genitally. We have homologous areas between the prostate and the G-spot, the clitoris and the penis; there's even a homologue of the vagina deep in a man's prostate. Anal tissue is similarly sensitive in men and women. The nerve endings are distributed around the head of the clitoris and the corona of the penis essentially in just the same way. So all this men-are-from-Mars, women-are-from-Venus nonsense is just that. There are plenty of social, and some biological, differences between males and females in our culture, but the way our genitals are built is the smallest of those differences, not the largest.

SOLANO: We don't carry desensitizing products. These items numb the area—the goal being for men to stay erect, even if it means completely giving up sensation. It's something we have to discuss with customers all the time: why we don't carry them and why it is important to retain sensation. We want to teach people that the mission is to feel the pleasure and really be able to broaden their horizons beyond [the notion] that the erection is the one and only goal.

QUEEN: Often what they're thinking is, "If I could last long enough, you could come." For many of those couples, longer intercourse is not going to make any difference in orgasm for the woman. What *will* work is a toy, a different approach to lovemaking, more of a focus on direct clitoral stimulation, either her or him putting a hand down between their bodies while they're having intercourse and adding some clitoral stimulation. And this whole notion that it all hangs on whether or not he can stay hard long enough . . .

MAN'S GUIDE: The pressure on both parties is ridiculous.

QUEEN: I write an advice column, and often I get orgasm questions: "How do I come? I can't come. I can't come with *him*." Turning orgasm into a problem instead of a peak of pleasure almost guarantees that you won't have that pleasure. Focusing so much mentally on having an orgasm is usually a recipe for not—you end up thinking yourself into ongoing sexual problems. That's one of the reasons that the guys who find Viagra useful needed it in the first place. When people start playing with toys, as opposed to "using marital aids," they can start to get past that. They can shift the definition more toward sensual exploration. There's more to it than just intercourse. There's more to it than just orgasm.

perfect figures

AND YOUR EX
IS ONLY RESPONSIBLE
FOR HALF OF THEM.

Number of sex acts
that occur every day:
120 million

MAN'S GUIDE: Supposedly, many sex-toy buyers are conservative Christians trying to preserve their marriages.

QUEEN: A surprising number of Republican married women, according to the statistics I have seen.

SOLANO: Some of our top-five states that we get the most sales from are also some of the most conservative. Outside of New York and California, Texas houses the largest number of our mail-order shoppers.

QUEEN: In Texas, it's illegal to own more than a few sex toys because it's considered intent to distribute.

MAN'S GUIDE: Didn't Good Vibes sponsor an emergency airlift of vibrators to the state of Alabama? What brought that on?

QUEEN: That was a fabulous, consciousness-raising publicity stunt. There are several states that criminalize sex-toy sales or sex-toy purchase and ownership. Most of these states have had these provisions in their laws for quite a long time; Alabama just added their provision about 2 years ago. Mostly those statutes go way back, well before sodomy laws started to get challenged. We wanted to draw national attention to the idea that people's sex lives were being monitored and affected by the state. There are people in Alabama suing the state over it. We wanted to declare our support for them and help in any way we could.

After the first round of PR, in order to up the ante a little bit, we figured that if the courts decide that vibrators are going to stay illegal, we would do an emergency airlift. Because it was a humanitarian crisis, after all.

The idea was really for us to use our PR clout and our size because the Alabama plaintiffs were tiny, women-run businesses without very much ability to speak to news organizations. And the ACLU was supporting them. It was totally fabulous because the ACLU usually doesn't involve itself in cases like this. This is the first we had heard of the ACLU getting involved in something like a sex-toy ban. We're still waiting to hear what the final word is going to be.

MAN'S GUIDE: What's the reasoning behind these laws?

QUEEN: Conservatives think sex toys are lewd and obscene.

MAN'S GUIDE: These are the same people who don't want the government in *their* business, but they think it's okay if it intrudes in the sex-toy business. Ironic, huh?

> **QUEEN:** They probably would rather that the government didn't see what was in their nightstand, either.
>
> Most conservatives are not very libertarian when it comes to sex. They're mostly libertarian when it comes to economic and other kinds of government regulations. So they may want to be able to drive 75 miles per hour on the freeway, but they don't think it's okay . . .

MAN'S GUIDE: . . . to have sex in the car while driving 75?

> **QUEEN:** Well, realistically speaking, that isn't a good idea. You should pull over to a rest area. Or just go home.
>
> But yeah, you're right. They were writing a new omnibus obscenity law in Alabama, trying to think of everything they might want to arrest somebody for that was sex-related.

MAN'S GUIDE: Joyce, you're the official Good Vibes toy buyer. What do you look for in a good sex toy?

> **SOLANO:** My job essentially is to go through the dozens of toy samples that get sent to me. Or I pore through catalogs. It's challenging because they're marketed as adult novelties. Craftsmanship, skills, materials, [and] labor often really aren't a priority. We have to know, first of all: Does it work? Not just work functionally, but does it *work*—does the battery last more than 5 seconds? So we actually test each and every vibrator before we ship it out.

MAN'S GUIDE: You mean turn it on? Or actually, well, test it?

> **SOLANO:** Turn it on, with the batteries in it. Our review process here does involve trying it out and writing a detailed review. Most other stores just base their choices on what the woman on the box looks like.

MAN'S GUIDE: So different staff members volunteer for this?

> **QUEEN:** It's a perk!

MAN'S GUIDE: What are they looking for?

SOLANO: Is it innovative? Is it high-quality? Is it nonoffensive in shape? We stay away from toys that are, like, a mold of a porn star's vagina—that are just body parts, pubic hair. Disembodied.

The staff essentially decides what we carry, because they tell me how they liked it. Did it work? Did it do what it was supposed to do? How was it used? What are the safety issues involved? Things like: Are there wires sticking out? Does it get too hot? We try to stick with things that are functional. There's a whole arena of novelty items that are more like gag stuff. We say that we offer the "hardware" of sex toys.

MAN'S GUIDE: What do you consider to be "gag stuff"?

QUEEN: Wind-up penises that hop across the desk. You know, cock or breast mugs. Something you would get for somebody to open at an office party specifically to embarrass them. They might have a cute factor, but they don't have a function factor.

SOLANO: Our focus has been on carrying items that will stimulate somebody. That will lubricate somebody. That will be an effective barrier. And our review process is pretty extensive. When somebody sends me a sample, it can take us a couple of weeks to make a decision. We put it through the ringer. And so we're able to say the negative and positive things about it and be honest with customers.

MAN'S GUIDE: How many products cross your desk—or hop across it—in, say, a month?

SOLANO: In any given month it could be 50, 60 samples. Out of those, there are only three or four things I end up choosing.

In the past year or so, we've seen a trend to make things more technologically advanced. Toys have features that are more innovative than in the past. The packaging has also gotten better. We generally don't use traditional industry packaging since it can be offensive. We try to buy our toys in bulk and sell them in plain plastic bags.

QUEEN: The [traditional] packages will say things that aren't true. They'll make unrealistic claims. And they'll sometimes call the toy things we consider offensive. There are race-related names, for instance, that African-American customers might find insulting. We don't think it sends the message we want our business to send. And yet sometimes the item itself, once you take the packaging away, is a fine little sex toy.

SOLANO: They're starting to get the message. At last year's Adult Novelty Manufacturer's Expo, they unveiled some lines that were really different in terms of packaging and materials. They've cloned iMac designs, added flashier colors and features like LED digital controllers. If you go to Toys R Us to see children's toys, you'll find neat gadgets and clever technology. And you start to realize that vibrator technology, as simple as it is, is probably 30 years behind.

MAN'S GUIDE: Why is that?

SOLANO: Maybe they don't want to invest the money. They want to stay cheap because it's for "novelty" use and because it'll sell anyway.

QUEEN: And many of them are fundamentally conservative. They're guys who inherited the business from their dad, some of them. It's wacky to think of this as a family business, but in many cases it is. And they're people who don't necessarily use toys themselves in their private lives. They're people who, when somebody like us starts to talk about why their G-spot toy can't actually do G-spot stimulation [for anatomical reasons], they'll say, "Huh?" Many of them are also uninterested in sexuality on the level that we try to speak for it every day.

MAN'S GUIDE: Are there any progressive toy makers out there?

SOLANO: There are. The small companies especially. Companies that have been very influenced by women, either in the design phase or at the ownership level. A lot of the folks making silicone, making the dildos. Just a couple in the vibrator area. Good Vibrations also plans on manufacturing its own toys in the near future.

perfect figures

WE'LL TAKE THE M3 INSTEAD, THANK YOU.

Percentage of couples who spend more than $50,000 on their weddings: 17

MAN'S GUIDE: Why dildos and not vibrators?

QUEEN: The technology of the vibrator side of things is just more expensive. People don't often make new vibrators in their garages. They have to find funding to start a whole new manufacturing process, or they have to sell their idea to one of the big guys. They may wind up watering it down to make it a little bit more like the things they already know how to make and are tooled up for. So there's a conservatism in manufacturing that you don't find in silicone or dildos, where so many of them are made by cottage industries.

> **❝ People who throw kisses are hopelessly lazy. ❞**
>
> —Bob Hope

SOLANO: Unfortunately, they also bring the higher prices because they're not making assembly-line products. Sometimes they're hard to support because first-time buyers at the stores might say, "I'll just buy the cheapie thing."

MAN'S GUIDE: What's an ideal toy you'd like to see made?

SOLANO: It's like food: One day you're into Chinese, one day in the mood for Italian. It's different for everybody. So there's not one shape or design that I think would be an across-the-line ideal. But we have a toy called the Hitachi Magic Wand, and we always say it's the Cadillac of vibrators. It's by far the best-selling toy for us. Hitachi is a large appliance manufacturer. And we can honestly say to somebody, "Fifteen to 20 years from now, that vibe will still be going."

MAN'S GUIDE: What toy would you suggest for men, either to use for their own pleasure or with women?

QUEEN: I would suggest that every man have at least a good-quality battery vibrator in his bag of tricks somewhere, if not a full electric plug-in. It's an appliance—and that's what we have an outlet by the bed for.

QUICKIES

ONCE IS ENOUGH

Don't worry about making a heroic stand in the bedroom. According to studies, bringing your partner to orgasm once a night may be all it takes to satisfy her. German researchers found that after orgasm, most women's bodies release hormones that may trigger a drop in sexual desire. "We believe that it's like a built-in on/off switch for sexual desire," says Michael Exton, Ph.D., one of the study authors. Differences in the hormonal response may explain why some women are ready to go again right away, while others like to cuddle.

ORDINARY HABITS
MAKE EXTRAORDINARY SEX

Dates, vacations, and all-night sex marathons are important, but the real bonding with your partner takes place during the little things. A peck on the cheek, a quick goodbye on the way to work, and even 5 minutes of chit-chat before bed each night help bring you closer together and may lead to better sex, according to William Doherty, Ph.D., a professor of family social science at the University of Minnesota in St. Paul, who has written almost a dozen books on family studies and family therapy.

"In order to survive and thrive, a relationship needs to have specific, regularly scheduled rituals," he says. "These are mutually decided upon times when both you and your partner must spend time together, but away from other people, including your children. It's what creates intimate bonds and keeps feelings of love alive."

If they forgo such rituals, couples tend to drift apart and marriages and relationships start to feel like they're on auto-pilot. And that, Doherty says, is what leads to lying, cheating, dishonesty, unhappiness, and ultimately separation or divorce. "It doesn't take much time to really make a difference. Talking after supper, running errands together, just sitting in the hot tub, or lying in bed together for 5 minutes before getting ready for work can all help to nurture a relationship, and keep it at its height of passion and commitment." The only rule: your rituals have to be personal. You can't talk logistics, or problem solving, or even finances.

ASK THE SEX DOC

Q: *After being separated for 3 months, my wife and I just got back together. Though neither of us slept around, things still feel awkward in bed. How do I get my sex life back to normal?*
—K. L., Houston

A: No matter what caused the split, your wife needs to receive, not give. Try this: Give her the best oral sex she's ever had. Do it slow, do it fast, make circles—hell, make hexagons. Just stay submerged until she grabs your ears like they're bullhorns and demands that you have sex with her. Nothing says "I care" quite like a charitable tongue. It's better than Hallmark.

Q: *I've always known my wife was adventurous, but I was shocked when she recently asked me to slap her bottom during sex. Now, she keeps suggesting even kinkier things. How far will this go? Should I worry?*
—R. B., Terre Haute, Indiana

A: Frankly, most guys can't get their partners to do anything interesting during sex. They'd love to be in your shoes—not to mention your bed.

As long as your wife's turn-ons are playful and good-natured, there's nothing wrong with them. "Until your wife's desire to be spanked starts to dominate your entire sex life, then there's nothing to worry about," says California sex therapist John D. Perry, Ph.D., director of www.drgspot.net.

True, it could escalate: light slapping today, leather whips and chains tomorrow. But that's relatively unlikely. "A person may have a seed planted within him that predisposes him to certain types of behavior, but exploring those desires now and then doesn't usually lead to them becoming more extreme," says Perry.

The Sex Doc is a fictional character.
The actual advice was provided by a variety of
medical doctors and other qualified experts.

4

SURVIVE
THE WAR
OF THE SEXES

Notice we don't say win *the war of the sexes. That's by design. In this war, there is no winning. There's just losing or, we hope, surviving. And unlike today's trendy, reality-based survivor shows, there is no million-dollar prize to walk away with. Instead, you're duking it out for a lifetime of relative peace and happiness. Which we think is a lot more satisfying in the long run than the million-dollar prize. And you don't have to kill a pig with your bare hands for a chance at it. All you have to do is make an effort to listen, understand, sympathize, and listen some more.*

On second thought, maybe killing the pig is the easier route.

In this section, we'll tell you how to survive this war—without losing the inner instinct that makes you a man.

TOP TEN

Things You Should Never Apologize For

1 Looking at a beautiful woman . . .

1½ . . . through binoculars

2 Waking her when you get up early for work . . .

2½ . . . or to go fishing

3 Coming too soon—it's a compliment!

4 Never being serious

5 Falling asleep on the couch

6 Wanting oral sex . . .

6½ . . . while driving

7 Not caring where the love seat and china cabinet go

8 Being a lousy Lamaze coach

9 The wet spot

10 Not knowing when to apologize

MUST READS

Buy Into Manhood

If you want to understand the female gender, it's not a bad idea to know a thing or two about your own. Unlike women, who reinvent their role in society once every few decades, men play more or less the same game as caveman ancestors. Go out and find food, bring it home, watch fur-swathed men play catch with a pig femur, have sex, and call it a night. Okay, so today it's Lycra-clad athletes playing catch with a pigskin, but the basics remain the same. This excerpt from The Men's Health Longevity Program *by the editors of* Men's Health *Books (Rodale, 2001) reminds you who you are.*

Try this exercise: Pick the one adjective from the list below that you would most like people to use in describing you. Not too long ago, we at *Men's Health* put the same task before 1,000 middle-aged men from across America. We'll tell you the results in a little bit.

- Athletic
- Reliable
- Sexual
- Capable
- Resourceful
- Spiritual
- Creative

- Respected
- Strong
- Handsome
- Sensitive
- Successful
- Intelligent

Scientists have confirmed what we men have long suspected: We are cavemen living in a modern world. And Adrian Targett is the living proof.

DNA tests conducted by scientists at Oxford University in England in the spring of 1997 found that Targett, a history teacher, is a direct descendant of Cheddar Man, a 9,000-year-old skeleton found less than a mile from Targett's home in England.

"My wife says that's why I like my steak rare," quips Targett.

Targett—and the average red-blooded male reading this book—has far more in common with his fossilized forefather than just a taste for red meat. "It's very difficult to find differences between someone who lived 10,000 years ago and someone at present," explains David Glenn Smith, Ph.D., professor of anthropology at the University of California, Davis. Dr. Smith is an expert in one of Cheddar Man's peers: Kennewick Man, a 9,300-year-old skeleton found in the state of Washington. "Emotionally and intellectually, we evolved to our present form a very long time ago," says Dr. Smith.

But make no mistake, we men proffer no apologies for our primitive wiring. We relish it. Manhood gives us ancient delights. We proudly bay at the moon. We drag our knuckles, grunt with glee, grab on to things that are conveniently at arm's length. We pursue the opposite sex. We compete. And, since time immemorial, we've more or less taught our sons to do the same.

We are imprinted with Pleistocene memories, says Dr. Smith, memories left over from the birth of mankind that make us act and respond much as our primitive ancestors did. But just as we hold the traits of a caveman, so did he have imbedded within him the genetic blueprint of a modern man. Ancient man had a noble, greater side, as do his sons of today.

"Men strive," says George H. Hartlaub, M.D., of the University of Colorado Health Sciences Center. "We always move, we always look for the better way. That is profound in us."

That drive has led men to scale Mount Everest simply because it's there and to descend to the ocean's floor to find the Titanic. It has inspired and informed Shakespeare's sonnets, Emerson's mystical meditations, and Chandler's hard-boiled prose. It has given us the Sistine Chapel, the Taj Mahal, and the

This We Know

Some things are just hardwired into a man's makeup. We hold truths like these to be self-evident.

- Just because we're adults now doesn't mean we can't actively seek out the banana with the sticker on it.

- Our penises are *never* to be referred to as cute.

- Fashion czars be damned: Paisley ties will never go out of fashion, for the simple reason that nothing else hides food stains as well.

- A true barber never has the word *curls* in his shop's name.

- Just because we know how to replace a belt in a washing machine doesn't mean we know how to do the laundry.

- There are two kinds of women: the kind you suck your gut in for and the kind you don't.

- Iced coffee makes about as much sense to us as hot peanut butter.

- We're not being deliberately nasty when we leave the toilet seat up. If we were being deliberately nasty, we'd take it *off*.

Empire State Building. It has blessed us with lasting images of Babe Ruth at bat, Michael Jordan soaring to unimagined heights, and Muhammad Ali floating like a butterfly, stinging like a bee.

It is, in a very real sense, what makes us men.

Men in Modern Times

As much as we enjoy our male heritage, the simple fact remains that although we're virtually identical to our long-dead forefathers, the world around us bears little resemblance to theirs. We require an amazing number of skills to wend our way through modern life.

Famed science fiction writer Robert Heinlein put it this way:

> *A human being should be able to change a diaper,*
> *plan an invasion, butcher a hog, conn a ship,*
> *design a building, write a sonnet, balance accounts,*
> *build a wall, set a bone, comfort the dying, take orders,*
> *give orders, cooperate, act alone, solve equations,*
> *analyze a new problem, pitch manure, program a*
> *computer, cook a tasty meal, fight efficiently, die gallantly.*
> *Specialization is for insects.*

While most of us aren't called upon these days to plan an invasion (except for the occasional midnight refrigerator raid) or pitch manure, you get the idea. No man is complete without a solid arsenal of guy skills to call his own. And no man should ever apologize for practicing these skills.

A Man's Man

"What we really want and need from our fathers, our teachers, [and] our men friends is that they see us as manly—as a man's man, as a man among men," says Michael Kimmel, Ph.D., sociology professor at the State University of New York at Stony Brook. "That's very, very important to us. I think it's the crucial theme in masculinity."

Men continue to ask the hard questions and probe for what it means to truly be a man during moments of crisis and transition, whether personal or societal. So where do we find the state of manhood today? We're glad you asked. Ronald F. Levant, Ed.D., dean of the center for psychological studies at Nova Southeastern University in Ft. Lauderdale and author of *Masculinity Reconstructed*, asked that very same question in a study he conducted. Here is what he found:

- Men have loosened up a lot concerning what they consider appropriate men-only and women-only behavior. We guys now believe that males can enjoy needlecraft and wear bracelets without it threatening their masculinity. We will, however, tease the hell out of guys who do that stuff.

- Men reject the old stereotype of the strong, silent type. Those in the study said that expressing emotions such as fear, worry, and love for their fathers was perfectly acceptable. John Wayne, we love you, we miss you, but we don't want to be you.

- Men are no longer expected to be studs all the time, eager whenever an opportunity for sex comes up. We are more inclined to connect sex with intimacy.

- Men are beginning to realize that achievement isn't the only thing that matters, and we are more willing to share power and status with women. Plus, it's nice to have that extra paycheck.

- Men are still committed to the idea that masculinity and self-reliance are closely related, but now it's okay, for example, to ask for help changing a tire. The guys in the survey disagreed with the statement, "A man should never doubt his judgment."

- Men still value the traits of strength, courage, and aggression, but we discriminate between healthy and unhealthy forms of aggression.

- There are signs that men have worked free enough of homophobia to disagree fairly strongly with the statement that a man should end a friendship with another man if he finds out the other man is a homosexual.

This brings us to our exercise. Here, in order of the most- to least-

SEX ✝ TRENDS

HER JOB MAKES YOU SICK

Having your wife work overtime gives you more time to play poker, plus a nice cushion for your losses. But University of Chicago research shows that she should scale back. Men whose wives worked less than 40 hours reported having the best health, while husbands of women who worked overtime saw their health decline by more than 25 percent over a 3-year period.

selected adjectives, are the words the men we surveyed wanted used to describe them: reliable, capable, respected, successful, creative, resourceful, intelligent, athletic, sensitive, spiritual, strong, handsome, and sexual. We think that makes a pretty good statement about manhood today.

We have nothing to be ashamed of. Sure, you should define who you are in terms of family, work, even the cosmos. But when every layer of meaning and purpose is stripped away, ultimately, you are a man. And that alone is something that should make you proud.

In fact, now is a better time than ever to be a man. Ignore the whining and finger-pointing that comes from various male-bashing corners. At no other time in history have we been as free to be exactly the kind of man we want to be. At no other time has the definition of manhood embraced so many meanings.

The Crying Game

One of the reasons that women are more likely than men to shed tears has nothing to do with emotions. Biologically, women have higher levels of the hormone prolactin, which primarily helps in the production of milk. Crying is one way to release excess quantities of prolactin.

About 80 percent of men report that they never or hardly ever cry, while the same percentage of women say they cry on a regular basis. According to one study, men are eight times less likely than women to cry when they are yelled at and nine times less likely to cry at sentimental gatherings. We're also less inclined to use tears manipulatively.

When men do cry, it is often framed in terms of their roles as provider, protector, warrior, athlete, husband, father, and team player. Male tears are more inclined to express experiences of pride, bravery, loyalty, victory, and defeat. Tears are not just more probable in those circumstances, they're almost expected. "I don't think I would like a man who is incapable of enough emotion to get tears in his eyes," said General Norman Schwarzkopf, of Desert Storm fame.

Enjoy it, revel in it, be proud of it, and go get 'em. We would slap you on the backside if we could.

What Do Women Want?

Funny thing about women: Just when you think you have figured her out—or at least made some progress—she goes and changes. We suspect she does it to keep you on your toes. Your task: to try and keep up. In this excerpt from Command Respect *(Rodale, 1998), Perry Garfinkel and Brian Paul Kaufman tell you how to be a nimble partner to the woman you love.*

The question even left Sigmund Freud, the father of psychoanalysis, scratching his scalp. "The great question that has never been answered," the Austrian pondered back in the early part of the 20th century, "and which I have not yet been able to answer, despite my 30 years of research into the feminine soul, is: What does a woman want?"

Little could he have imagined that in the 1960s, the Queen of Soul would spell out (and belt out) the answer to his query. "R-E-S-P-E-C-T," Aretha Franklin sang. "Find out what it means to me." *Dat vazn't zo deefeecult, vazit, Herr Freud?*

Or was it? We have spent the last 40 years of the 20th century trying to find out what respect means to women as a gender. And more to the point, you have spent the last 7, 15, or 25 years trying to figure out what it means to the one woman you promised you'd be with 'til death do you part.

perfect figures

WE GET THE 2:1 RATIO, BUT CAN SOMEBODY EXPLAIN THE EXTRA 67 CENTS?

For every dollar spent on prostate-cancer research, $2.67 is spent on breast-cancer research

He Said, She Said

You're not to be blamed if you haven't figured out where all the pieces fit in the Rubik's Cube of romance. If it's any solace—and we believe confusion loves company—a survey conducted by Roper Starch Worldwide for the 1995 Virginia Slims Opinion Poll reflects some contradictory trends regarding respect and marriage. Take a peek.

● On the one hand, 43 percent of women said their marriages had improved over the years, up 9 percent from 1990. But on the other, the percentage of women who said they were "very satisfied" with their relationships with men dropped from 56 percent in 1990 to 49 percent in 1995.

● While 74 percent of women and 73 percent of men agreed that men were more involved in their children's lives than they used to be, 48 percent of women resented the way child-care duties were still unevenly divided and 47 percent resented the amount of time they spent keeping the family organized.

● Most women and men (81 and 80 percent, respectively) said that they admired a man who shows his sensitive side. But both women and men (84 and 85 percent, respectively) agreed that men were just as competitive as ever, and 57 percent of women and 43 percent of men thought men were still self-centered.

● While 72 percent of men said they had become more understanding of women's needs, only 61 percent of women felt that men understood them better.

● In spite of 25 years of progress toward equal treatment of men and women in society, 84 percent of women still believed that "regardless of changes that may have occurred, women still have more restriction in life than men do." And 77 percent of women agreed that "while sexual discrimination is more subtle and less open, it remains a serious problem today." Seventy-nine percent of women and 70 percent of men believed that some men still find it hard to think of women as equals.

● There's a discrepancy about how much men are reexamining their behavior. While 70 percent of men said that women were too quick to call them sexist, only 57 percent of women thought that women were too quick to label men sexist. Also, 62 percent of men said that they were questioning their own macho roles, while 54 percent of women said that they believed men were reexamining those roles.

● The bottom line: 70 percent of both genders agree that "most men are confused about what women expect of them nowadays."

This brings us full circle to Sigmund Freud and Aretha.

What women want is for men to simply respect that being a woman is complicated and complex, a maze of mixed messages, suggests James Sniechowski, Ph.D., a Los Angeles-based counselor for men and co-author with his wife, Judith Sherven, Ph.D., of the book *The New Intimacy.*

"Men will earn women's respect more if they appreciate that no matter how far women have come since the women's movement of the 1960s, they are still raised to be second-class citizens and are still often treated that way," Dr. Sniechowski says. "Also, married women in their upper 30s, 40s, and beyond struggle between wanting to be taken care of and wanting independence."

To earn their respect, he suggests, we need to avoid getting caught in the

Arguing with Respect

Yes, women want men to listen to them. But they also want men to speak their minds. "Women respect men who don't shut down, withdraw, or pull away when issues come up," says the University of Denver's Dr. Scott Stanley. "That infuriates them."

The problem is that "what women call a discussion, men often call a fight," observes Diane Sollee, director of the Coalition for Marriage, Family, and Couples Education, a coalition based in Washington, D.C., that serves as a clearinghouse to promote education for couples. As a means of self-preservation, husbands tend to "stonewall it" when they think women are trying to pick a fight, contends Daniel Goleman, Ph.D., a behavioral sciences writer for the *New York Times* and author of *Emotional Intelligence*. The reason: it takes men less emotional negativity than women to trigger the secretion of adrenaline into their bloodstreams, which then increases their heart rates. "The stoic male imperturbability may represent a defense against feeling emotionally overwhelmed," Dr. Goleman says.

Dr. Stanley offers three quick tips for fighting with your wife while still respecting each other.

❶ **Separate the issues from the person.** It's possible that the person you love may not like the same shade of purple you do. She may be a Democrat while you are a Republican. She says "po-tay-to," you say "po-tah-to."

Don't call the whole thing off. People are not defined by their opinions. Assaulting others' personalities because they don't agree with your point of view shows no respect for the individual.

❷ **Avoid generalizations.** "Always" and "never" are rarely accurate assessments of how frequently or infrequently people do things. "You backlash of their confusion. Sometimes we need to stand our ground, to hold it steady as she goes.

How Do You Spell Respect?

When it comes to keeping love alive in a long-term relationship, there is no issue more crucial than respect, says Scott Stanley, Ph.D., co-director of the Center for Marital and Family Studies at the University of Denver and co-author of *Fighting for Your Marriage.* "Over the years, I've seen that women have difficulty maintaining their attraction to men they've lost respect for," he says. "Men should never assume that just because they are married, they've earned that respect once and for all and can go to pot, so to speak."

Preserving a lasting love, based on mutual respect, requires a certain vigilance. Your lawn won't flourish unless you keep watering it. Feed your relationship with respect and it will thrive. Here's how.

always leave the cap off the toothpaste tube" may be true more times than not, but you are not giving your wife positive reinforcement for that one out of 10 times she remembers putting it back on. And she will be sure to remind you of that one time she did.

3 **Stay on point.** It's not fair to bring up the time she met her old boyfriend for drinks while you're arguing about who forgot to close the windows before a rainstorm. Resolve one conflict at a time. Perhaps it's better to let sleeping dogs (and old boyfriends) lie, anyway.

◗ Let her breathe.
Despite the myth of men's inability to be intimate, "a lot of men feel intimacy has to be . . . constant and all-pervasive," says Mark Epstein, M.D., a psychiatrist in Manhattan and author of *Thoughts Without a Thinker.* "That becomes claustrophobic." Many men today "have difficulty respecting the separateness or autonomy of the person they're involved with," he says. "They expect her to be catering to their every emotional need."

When she doesn't meet his needs, he pouts and withdraws or gets aggressive and even more demanding. Women have their own needs and identities that are not tied to the men in their lives, Dr. Epstein says. Men must learn to respect that. In other words, give her space.

◉ Let her grow.

She used to party hard. Now she's into meditation. Her idea of healthy eating once meant ordering a Big Mac because it had lettuce and pickles. Now she's dabbling with macrobiotics. Her values are changing, and it scares you. You may be thinking that this is not the woman you married.

Welcome to the human species. This is called evolution; it's called growing and changing, and it's supposed to happen to normal, healthy human beings. "We stereotype our wives," says Dr. Sniechowski. "After 20 years, we assume that she can't possibly say something that will surprise you."

HEY, THAT'S MY BACON!

Percentage of Americans who don't tell their spouses they received a raise: 36

◉ Embrace change.

How many times has a buddy come to you with that sad, confused, clueless look in his eyes and told you that it came out of left field when she claimed she had outgrown him and left him? You want to say, "What did you expect? How long did you think she'd be patient while you kept reading *Success* magazine after she had subscribed to *Simple Living*?" What you should say to yourself is, "Thank God it wasn't me." And promise yourself that you'll stay in tune with your partner's changing interests and remain open to new ideas.

◉ Be your own man.

Accept the fact that you can never be everything she wants. She doesn't necessarily want you to be, anyway. "Many women are caught in a terrible bind," Dr. Sniechowski says. They're fighting off the idealized 1950s *Ozzie and Harriet* model as well as the cynical 1990s version typified by *Married . . . with Children.*

If a man is too sensitive, he's a wimp. If he's not sensitive enough, he's a patriarchal troglodyte. What's a regular guy to do?

Despite her wavering, "claim your own identity," Dr. Sniechowski says. That's what she wants and respects. Don't buckle under the pressure of every gender redefinition you read about in *USA Today*. Stick to your guns. She'll respect you more.

◉ Drive on a two-way street.

Dr. Sniechowski sees another ramification of the mixed messages that both sexes send each other. Men tell him, "She said she wanted me to share my vulnerabilities, but when I did, she freaked out and seemed to question my masculinity." Women can't have it both ways, he says. Dr. Sniechowski offers tough-love advice: "Demand it. Say, 'I will not *not* be human.' If the context is mutual respect, then as long as you are presenting her with who you are, she needs to accept that part of you, too."

Dr. Sniechowski says that he and his wife, also a psychologist, resort to a caveat when they don't see eye-to-eye on how the other should behave: "I accept you exactly the way you are, *and* I reserve the right to want you to be different."

● Take time.

By now we know that women want to talk *and* want to be heard. But that takes time. As much as you'd love to sit and gab, there's stuff that needs to get done: lawns to mow, calls to return, and other manly responsibilities. Strike a compromise. All talks don't have to be intense, suggests Dr. Stanley. Spend 10 minutes here, 10 minutes there. "But make them a powerful 10 minutes," he recommends. Don't keep glancing over at the game on the tube while pretending to give her your full attention. "Even these short spurts are longer than some couples allow themselves," he says, and they serve as short-term pressure-reducers until longer blocks of time can be scheduled.

● Play ball.

Of course, those longer periods don't just materialize magically, says Dr. Stanley. He suggests the two of you agree whether you'll be discussing heavy issues or just enjoying playtime. If you opt for play—even adults deserve recess—agree not to discuss the mundane, nagging details of your shared life (like, "Did you call the refrigerator repairman?" or "Have you finished the financial aid forms for Junior?"). Save that for a meeting in which you clear the deck of everything but domestic concerns.

● Cut out the cutting remarks.

Little put-downs show clear disrespect. Those negative comments can do more to corrode a relationship than positive efforts can do to keep it strong and vibrant, Dr. Stanley warns. He particularly singles out the man

SEX TRENDS

THEY HAD TO STUDY THIS?

A study of 44 couples at Brandeis University found that nagging doesn't work; leading by example does. In other words, if she wants you to drop a few pounds, she'd better start doing laps around the block herself. Meanwhile, have a beer.

who cuts down his wife in the company of other people. "This is a guy who doesn't have the *cojones* to tell her in private," he says. "He has been chewing on something for a while and doesn't have the guts to tell her more respectfully in private, so he does it in the safer context, where he knows she's not going to make a scene in front of friends or family."

His advice to men like this: grow up. "Get up the gumption to say that you'd like to discuss something that has been bothering you. But don't bring it up when it happens. Try to discuss it when you're not emotionally charged, when you're both in a supportive and loving mood." Then she'll understand that you're trying to respect the integrity of the relationship. If you continue to use sarcasm and cynicism and put-downs as your primary communications strategy, it's time to consult a professional, such as a therapist or psychologist, for help, says Dr. Stanley.

perfect figures

CLEARLY THEY DON'T KNOW YOUR KID.

Percentage of Americans who say boys are easier to raise: 53

Percentage who say girls are: 28

Percentage who say there's no difference: 14

Percentage of men who would rather have a boy if they could only have one child: 55

● **Be a happy hubby.**

Happy people have happier marriages, says Linda Dougherty, Ph.D., associate professor of gerontology and psychiatry at Virginia Commonwealth University in Richmond. Dr. Dougherty was part of a team that examined why some couples successfully go the distance. They found that marital satisfaction in couples married an average of 22 years was directly related to how "outgoing, warm, positive, gregarious, and ebullient" the partners were. Wives said that the more kind, considerate, and thoughtful their husbands were, the higher they rated the quality of their marriages.

"This is common sense," she admits. "People like being around people who are nice to them, have a positive outlook on life, and like and are liked by other people." Dr. Dougherty puts another spin on this obvious wisdom. Outgoing people focus on others, she notes. We all like having that attention focused on us; it makes us feel special, respected. (This would be especially true of women who feel that they are still not valued as first-class citizens.) She found in other studies that people who were more self-centered did not have happy marriages.

● **Be willing to work at it.**
Just because your life together isn't going as smoothly as a line in a greeting card doesn't mean that you're doing something wrong. "It's not simple," Dr. Sniechowski says. "Love is full of ambivalence and ambiguity. If it's rocky, you haven't made a mistake. In fact, you may be doing something right." That certainly is the case if you're venturing into deeper emotional waters. There's going to be a period where you're afraid that you're in over your head. But working through those times together will bring you closer and lead to a deeper, more satisfying relationship.

Know When She Wants It

Even if you skipped sex ed, you know the basics of the female menstrual cycle. Some days are good for sex, other days are bad. Some days she cries for no reason, others she pops Advils until she rattles like a maraca. And don't forget the days she breaks out the boxes of super-maxi-plus wonder pads. Beyond that, you let her *worry about it.*

Big mistake. Understand her cycles, says writer Alex James, and you're one step closer to understanding her. She'll give you anything you want—as long as you ask for it at the right time of the month.

We've discovered the key to domestic bliss, and it's as easy as 1, 2, 3. Well, actually, it's as easy as 1, 2, 3, 4 . . . all the way to 28. Why? Because there are 28 days in a woman's menstrual cycle, and her menstrual cycle is what really determines how things go between you.

For example, on Day 24 you should learn to duck. We talked to sex experts and discovered how the hormonal fluxes in a woman's body affect her moods—and your life—throughout the month. Then we created a handy schedule for you to consult when you want to know which days you're going to get sex, which days you're going to get yelled at, and which days you're going to get yelled at during sex.

● **Days 1 to 5: She's ready to iron and fold.**
What's happening to her: She may complain of cramps a few days before this, but this is where her menstrual cycle really starts. Her estrogen levels are dropping, so there's only a 2 percent chance she'll get pregnant if you have sex. That

would be great news, except you won't be having sex right now. Thanks to those low estrogen levels, she currently sees you as a large lump of cells in a stupid shirt.

Your strategy: Lack of estrogen can also trigger insomnia and restlessness, which is why many women feel the urge to clean and organize during these days, says Christiane Northrup, M.D., author of *Women's Bodies, Women's Wisdom.* Our suggestion: Forget about sex and point her to your filthy clothes.

● **Days 6 to 9: She's up for anything.**

What's happening to her: She's calmer and happier now because her body is saturated in feel-good hormones and endorphins. "That means she's more receptive to new and creative ideas," says Dr. Northrup.

Your strategy: Break out the new and creative ideas! This is the time to settle old disputes and get buy-in on your golf trip with the guys. You might also want to revisit your pool-table-in-the-living-room idea.

● **Days 10 to 14: She's horny.**

What's happening to her: A rise in the hormone androgen has rekindled her interest in sex. This causes the thin lining of mucus around her cervix—deep in her vagina at the entrance to the uterus—to become thin and watery. "Press it between your fingers and it's stringy, like glue," says Helen Mitchell, M.D., a gynecologist at University College in London. Actually, don't do that. She may take a swing at you.

Your strategy: Take Dr. Mitchell's word for it on the stringy-mucus thing and just worry about having great sex. Your woman's so ready, you won't need more than a minute of foreplay. "Set the mood in a few seconds by telling her how much you want to have sex with her," says Tara Roth Madden, author of *Romance on the Run—Quality Sex for Busy Couples.* Your pants should be off before you finish the sentence.

hot TIP

Maybe you should listen when your girlfriend complains about your favorite bar. Secondhand smoke raises the chances that her menstrual period will be painful, according to a Harvard study. Oh, well. You'll have to drink with the guys.

● **Day 15: She's really horny.**

What's happening to her: On the positive side, she craves sex because she's at her most fertile. On the negative side, the sex doesn't necessarily have to be with you. Research shows she's more likely to be unfaithful during this time. In one study, researchers observed 500 women in nightclubs and found that they were more likely to wear revealing clothes and send suggestive signals to men at this phase in their cycles. Naturally, the researchers still went home alone.

Your strategy: Don't let her out of the house by herself. Instead, take advantage of her adventurous mood by trying a new position in a new location. Have her sit on the couch (naked) with you (also naked) kneeling in front of her. Have her put her legs over your shoulders as you move close and enter her in front. The angle you create will target her G-spot for a quicker and more intense orgasm. That's good for you, bad for the couch.

● **Days 16 to 23: She's a lesbian.**

What's happening to her: Her estrogen level is dropping again, so she's less fertile. Research shows that during these 8 days, she's more attracted to feminine-looking men because they appear more nurturing. She's no longer looking for a strong man to provide sturdy genes and protection.

Your strategy: She wants a womanly man or a manly woman. Shave and put on some Melissa Etheridge.

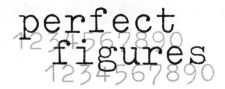

perfect figures

GET A SEX CHANGE
BEFORE *YOU* KILL HER.

Percentage of female murderers
who killed an intimate
or family member: 60

Percentage of male murderers:
20

Among women convicted
of killing their husbands,
percentage who receive
prison sentences: 81

Percentage of wife killers
who go to jail: 94

● ● ● ● ● ● ● ● ● ●

● **Days 24 to 28: She could crack at any moment.**

What's happening to her: Estrogen continues to fall as tantrum-provoking progesterone rises. This leads to premenstrual syndrome, during which she'll be extrasensitive to criticism, more neurotic about her looks, and more likely to throw a fit, or a Crock-Pot.

Your strategy: Play tennis or go for a run with her—vigorous exercise can reduce her symptoms. That way, if she "feels fat," at least she's doing something about it.

● **Days 26 to 28: She's craving ice cream and brownies.**

What's happening to her: Her estrogen and progesterone levels are falling as her body prepares to start the cycle all over again. Low levels of estrogen can cause her to crave high-fat foods such as chocolate, which studies show can elevate mood, but also tighten pants.

Your strategy: Indulge her cravings by taking her out to eat rather than bringing home a quart of Ben & Jerry's. The reason? She'll eat the entire tub—then blame you for letting her do it.

THE FUNNY PAGE

"Maybe you ought to consider making love in the morning—before you have a chance to piss each other off."

HELP ONLINE

TUNE UP YOUR RELATIONSHIP

Things running a little rough between you and the missus?
Better schedule a tune-up with the "relationship mechanic." He's a certified
family therapist from Australia who offers a personal question
and answer service, as well as fee-based, convenient "e-counseling"
in a private chat-room atmosphere. Couch not included.
www.relmechanic.com

BUILD A BETTER HOME LIFE

Run by a male psychotherapist from Maine, this site is a great resource
for couples serious about building a strong relationship. The bricks
and mortar used for this home-improvement project? Cool quizzes,
articles, workshops, and weekly relationship boosters all aimed
at improving a couple's communication and mutual understanding.
If you begin most of your conversations with "Honey, could you
wash/iron/clean/fold this for me, . . ." we suggest you log on fast.
www.couplesplace.com

PLANET OF THE APES

Best-selling author John Gray made a gazillion dollars by telling us what we
already knew: that men and women come from two different planets.
Now he runs this Web site (when he's not on the touring circuit, that is).
She doesn't understand your grunts? Tell her it's a Martian thing and have
her check out the site. There she can e-mail Dr. Gray her questions or find
tips on how to relate to your communication style. *You* may want to check
out the sex tips. While they don't sizzle, they may get you off the couch.
www.marsvenus.com

Disposable You:
Breaking Down the Feminism Myth

An Interview with Warren Farrell

Once there was a feminist named Warren Farrell. He was the only man elected three times to the board of directors of the National Organization for Women. He fielded job offers from universities all over the country. He struck lucrative publishing deals for his books. He owned two houses. He drove a Maserati.

All that changed when he started to ponder some unthinkable thoughts: What if the feminist movement wasn't really about equality and women weren't victims? What if it was built on giving opportunity to women largely at the expense of demonizing men and marginalizing dads, destroying any idea of fairness and common sense along the way? And what if one were to announce publicly that men were getting the short end of the stick in divorce, to the detriment of not only themselves but also their children?

Just asking those questions proved detrimental to Farrell. The teaching offers dried up. The publishing deals weren't nearly so lucrative. The Maserati? Replaced by an aging import. Defending men, it seems, is an exceedingly poor career move.

Does Farrell, the author of such notable books as Why Men Are the Way They Are, Father and Child Reunion, The Myth of Male Power, *and* Women Can't Hear What Men Don't Say, *wish he had chosen differently? Read for yourself.*

MAN'S GUIDE: You've taken a real battering over the past few years. Why are you getting hit so hard by women who once were allies?

FARRELL: When I question women's status as victims, it violates an instinct that has evolved among male and female animals and humans for millions of years—the instinct to win women's love by protecting them.

That instinct runs so deep it prevails even when that protection seduces women into remaining weak. Divorce has left millions of women unprotected. And the women's movement fulfilled the instinct to protect women by creating "options for protection": either by women protecting themselves, by getting exes to protect women, or by getting the government to be a substitute husband—[by getting] legislators to do collectively what a husband had failed to do individually.

The more that women could be seen as victims—the more special programs such as affirmative action, women-only scholarships, opportunities to join the armed services without obligations to register for the draft like boys do—the more these special programs could be justified.

I knew that if I challenged female victim power, I would be the enemy; but I felt the demonizing of men and false equality would do more harm than good. Not just to the family but also to children, which meant girls as much as boys.

MAN'S GUIDE: Go on about victim power and false equality.

FARRELL: Some examples include focusing on homeless women and thus providing homeless shelters especially for women, even when 85 percent of the homeless are men. Or believing that women are the more likely victims of domestic violence—which is not true—and thus doing nothing to fund shelters for men. Or creating affirmative-action programs for women because we believe women receive only 76 cents to men's dollar for the same work, when in fact they receive less, but not for the same work. For much different work: many fewer hours per week, less hazardous jobs, work in more desired locations, etcetera.

There's something very fundamental about when women say, "I need help, and I want more options," that we immediately open up and say, "Where do you need help, and what options do you need?" Women asked for protection from fathers, then husbands. From the government, God, or gurus. Men competed to be their protectors by competing to be the legislators, gurus, ministers, priests, rabbis, or warriors. Men competed to kill in war or "make a killing" on Wall Street. And of course, killing meant exposing themselves to being killed, which meant thinking of themselves as powerful by making themselves disposable.

Every society that has survived has had an unconscious investment in the disposability of its men. In the past, that was functional for survival. In the future, it is less needed for survival and must be questioned, because people who are trained to receive approval by being disposable can never really love themselves and be open and feeling husbands and fathers.

MAN'S GUIDE: You say divorce leaves women unprotected, but don't women usually initiate divorce?

FARRELL: Yes. To this day, two-thirds of the people who initiate divorce are women. Women were the first to go to therapists saying, "I'm unhappy with my life." These women weren't poor women—poor women couldn't afford therapists. They were usually women married to men successful enough to afford their wives the time and income to question their [lives]. This led to increased expectations that went unfulfilled: She had married a money machine, and now she wanted a nurturer/listener. So she filed for divorce. Then, as a single mom, she was too exhausted to fulfill her dreams of fulfillment, too needed by her children to easily let a new man into her closed circle. Men wanted younger women and didn't necessarily want another man's children. She felt disposable. She got angry.

MAN'S GUIDE: Perhaps it's natural that women's anger toward men and also men's anger toward women is shown in the way we act sexually. What is it about sex that creates all this baggage?

FARRELL: One thing is that the promise for many years was that women, in exchange for one act of sex, would be taken care of for a lifetime. That is, you weren't allowed to have sex before you were married. The purpose of that was to make sex so valuable that when you did have it, it was only available at the price of a man being willing to take care of that woman economically and take care of as many children as she and he bore together. So basically the promise of a woman's sexuality was an economically secure life ever after.

> ## hot TIP!
>
> *You made fun of her Hummel collection, and she winged one at your head. But that could be a good thing. "Teasing solves conflicts because it's an indirect way to prompt people to change," says Dacher Keltner, Ph.D., a researcher in California. Dr. Keltner has found that couples who kid each other about their conflicts like each other more.*

MAN'S GUIDE: Boy, it better be some good sex.

FARRELL: Yeah, right. Sex within that framework was looked at as being just fine. And sex for its own sake—sex for pleasure—was looked upon as threatening that framework. If a woman wanted to have sex just for herself, then the possibility was [that] she would end up having it with a male to whom she was not married. That would lead to children whom the society couldn't take care of.

MAN'S GUIDE: Yes, and up until the advent of decent birth control, that was very much the case.

FARRELL: And so our inheritance was to have sex outside of marriage be looked upon as being immoral and dirty—and criminal.

MAN'S GUIDE: Those attitudes are still very much with us and encouraged by some sectors of the population.

FARRELL: Absolutely. Female anger around sex is about a woman feeling, "When a man has sex with me, I should expect some things from that"—whether it's dinner or drinks or flowers or special considerations. If we want to move women and men to a place where they're truly equal, you cannot have women's sexuality mean more, be worth more, than men's.

MAN'S GUIDE: How likely is it that we'll reach such equality?

FARRELL: Well, the ability to adapt has come far in the last 50 years. Now there are millions of women who have sex to enjoy themselves. There's still a promise of the dinner, the drinks, the diamond. But most women do not expect a lifetime of economic security in exchange for an active sex life anymore.

We really have to understand how big a change that has been for women. And at the same time, how much resentment some women hold for that amount of leverage no longer being theirs—that other women are "giving it away for free."

> "Love is what we call the situation which occurs when two people who are sexually compatible discover that they can also tolerate one another in various other circumstances."
>
> —Marc Maihueird

MAN'S GUIDE: Do you think that part of the whole disposable-male idea is an unspoken value of stoicism? The ability to suck it up without complaining?

FARRELL: It is exactly the reason why men don't go to doctors. As for getting in touch with his feelings—the man who got in touch with his feelings on a football field didn't like the concussion he was getting. Or the dislocated shoulder. Then next week, he wasn't on the team. And the cheerleader was cheering for his replaceable part.

It works out in hundreds of other ways. The dot-commer in Silicon Valley who's in touch with his feelings, who doesn't work 70, 80, 90 hours a week—he's not the one who's the millionaire. The one who gets in touch with his feelings is going to be there 30 or 40 hours a week.

You ask women how much they would like to work in a week, and they usually say about 25 to 35 hours. And you look at the men who are most loved by women, and they're usually working 60 to 80 hours.

> **If a woman has to choose between catching a fly ball and saving an infant's life, she will choose to save the infant's life without even considering if there are men on base.**
>
> —Dave Barry

MAN'S GUIDE: That brings up an interesting point: the dichotomy between what women say they want and what they actually do want. They want the affectionate, emotionally secure man, but they also don't want a wimp.

FARRELL: They genuinely want both things. They want the man to be a contradiction in terms. Virtually nobody understands how both sexes fall in love with the members of the other sex who are least capable of loving.

Women fall in love with the men who are the most successful. But the men who are the most successful at work learn personality characteristics that are not helpful to them in their love life. We learn to be the soldier or the surgeon who disconnects from his feelings, or the lawyer who listens to his opponents just for the purpose of picking out the flaws in what his opponents are saying. Bring that home to your wife and you're dead.

Conversely, men are programmed to fall in love with the young female who doesn't know as much about love and intimacy as an older woman. The beautiful young woman goes into a self-serve gas station and station attendants compete to make it a full-service station just for her. She learns that she can get full service at self-service prices. And obviously, that sense of entitlement is not what creates a good marriage. In brief, then, everything that's biologically functional for "love" has become dysfunctional for a happy marriage.

perfect figures

THIS SURVEY WAS NOT TAKEN ON DEATH ROW.

Percentage of men who say that men are treated better in American society today: 41

Percentage of women who say that: 62

MAN'S GUIDE: Which would seem to explain why a guy who's able to admit his feelings often ends up complaining that he can't get a date.

FARRELL: Those were not the things to which women were biologically programmed to respond. We must work together to lovingly develop new methods of selecting each other, and our education system has to be about comprehending those new methods and communicating them.

MAN'S GUIDE: You once said in an interview with Salon.com: "We have more empathy for whales than males." That was a great line.

FARRELL: Thank you. "We care more about saving whales than saving males" is the normal way I say it.

MAN'S GUIDE: But in many ways, aren't men okay with that? Doesn't it go back to the stoicism we talked about?

FARRELL: That's the problem. Just like the women's movement had to train women to understand that they were competent to work in the workplace—that they could lift twice as much as they were told they could lift, that they could be involved in sports, that they could do all these things they're capable of doing—we have to teach men the same set of things.

MAN'S GUIDE: What, specifically, can men do to achieve this mission?

> **FARRELL:** The best way to start is getting our school system to have boys sit in groups, with teachers encouraging them to talk about their feelings; making it an okay thing to do at a very early age. Parents need to do the same thing with their kids. Today there are more boys brought up with that than ever. In fact, some boys, especially boys brought up by single mothers, are oftentimes so much that way they can't compete in the world. They're overprotected and overly sensitive.
>
> It's the job of parents and teachers themselves to learn that you can have the best of both worlds.

MAN'S GUIDE: Do you integrate the best of both worlds in your personal life?

> **FARRELL:** I think so. I can cry extremely easily. I can express my feelings very well. But I'm also able to say, "I've got to get this done for a little while. I've just got to push this out of the way and make this happen." Thus I write and produce.

MAN'S GUIDE: Is there anything we didn't talk about that's important in the evolving relationship between men and women?

> **FARRELL:** I could go into domestic violence, date rape, sexual harassment, the politics of housework, etcetera, etcetera. It's taken me five books to write all that down because of the depth. It's a lot of writing to rethink all that stuff. Perhaps if a reader wants to check out the table of contents of one of my books before investing in it, she or he can check www.warrenfarrell.com.

MAN'S GUIDE: Is the effort you put out and the criticism you receive worth it?

> **FARRELL:** I ask myself that question almost every day.

QUICKIES

SHE WINS, YOU WIN

Here's our idea of foreplay: Bet your wife that you'll beat her in a few friendly video games. The catch? You have to make sure she wins. A study in the journal *Addiction* reported that 32 women who played slot machines experienced changes in heart rate and body chemistry similar to those that occur during arousal—but only when they won.

DO OPPOSITES ATTRACT?

Yeah—they attract divorce lawyers. Studies of married couples reveal that we choose partners who are much like us. While men are attracted to partners who come from similar backgrounds (ethnic, religious, educational, or upbringing), we also look for partners who offset our personal defects.

HORMONES MADE ME DO IT

That midlife crisis isn't your fault, according to Italian research. Studies at the Institute of Psychology in Rome concluded that men are biologically programmed to fall in love again when they reach the age of 50. And while many may experience a resurgence in their feelings toward their wives, plenty more find their newfound passion is for a "younger model."

The researchers interviewed 3,000 red-blooded Romans and concluded that men go through several ages of love; from the "puppy" type experienced in their teens, to serious attachments in their 20s, then sexual exploration in their 30s and 40s, before reaching another "higher" level as they approach 50.

THERE ARE CHICK BOSSES?

Percentage of American men who would prefer to have a male boss: 45

Percentage who don't care: 35

ASK THE SEX DOC

Q: *Each time my wife and I have even a tiny argument, I get the cold shoulder every night for weeks. Is this normal? Is there a way to keep day-to-day disagreements out of our sex life?*
—A. W., CLEVELAND

A: One thing's for sure: Whatever she was mad about this morning, she won't forget it just because you're suddenly in the mood.

In fact, a British study shows that marital and psychological problems are the most likely cause of many sexual problems for women. After polling more than 1,700 Brits, researchers at Keele University found that women with at least one sexual complaint (like problems with arousal or orgasm) reported more than three times the rate of marital stress as sexually functional women. Men with rocky relationships had no additional problems in bed.

"For women, problems with the relationship can directly affect desire, and from there lead to physical sexual problems. But emotional factors aren't as important for a man's function," explains lead researcher Peter Croft, M.D., professor of epidemiology. The result? While you're ready and eager to make up, your wife can't stand the sight of you.

If it's really just an everyday spat that's extinguishing your wife's flame, let her talk it out. Resolving the argument to everybody's satisfaction is a step in the right direction. But be warned: you could have your work cut out for you. "A lot of times there are underlying issues that can't be worked out so easily. For women, a problem-free sex life depends on a positive marital environment, not just a temporary solution to the most recent argument," says Dr. Croft.

Q: *My wife has a small mouth, and during oral sex she sometimes scratches my penis with her teeth. How can I get her to modify her technique? I'm hesitant to say anything because, you know, I like oral sex.*
—T. S., MILWAUKEE

A: You're a wise man: No woman likes to be told her oral sex skills need work. In fact, the less said, the better. Instead of cringing, try letting out a mild "ouch," or a "gently," next time she goes a bit over-board. Or encourage her to try using more tongue. Tell her you'd like it if she licked you from bottom to top. When she gets to the head of your penis, ask her to use more suction—as long as her mouth's in a sucking position she'll be unable to bite down. Stick to positive mes-sages and new techniques—don't mention that there's anything wrong with her current method.

If she's still leaving bite marks, get yourself some protective padding. A company called Total Head Creations makes a gummy bear-like candy designed to be worn over a woman's teeth during oral sex. She'll be able to bite down as hard as she wants and all you'll feel is wet gum. It tastes good, too, and there's also one designed for a man to use on a woman. A pair costs $7.50 from www.headcandy.net.

Q: *After sex, my girlfriend seems to have a problem with gas—but from a slightly different part of her anatomy.* **She gets embarrassed and I don't know what the heck it is. What can I tell her?**
—S. C., PHOENIX

A: During intercourse, her vagina expands both in width and in length as the cervix lifts up. When you pull out, air can get trapped in there, forming little pockets when she returns to normal size. These air pockets need to escape, so when she stands up, she may make a noise like a passel of cowboys after a chili-eating contest. Smile endearingly and explain that it's a normal by-product of sex. (Maybe she'll be more forgiving of *you* next time.)

The Sex Doc is a fictional character.
The actual advice was provided by a variety of
medical doctors and other qualified experts.

ORCHESTRATE
SIZZLING
DATES

Here's something the folks at Ticketmaster don't want you to know: A scorching date isn't about taking her to the biggest show or the most expensive concert. It's not about eating at the fanciest restaurant. It's not about blowing a huge wad of cash or arriving in a fancy car. It's about the little things. The things you say and the way you treat her. It's about atmosphere and chemistry. Whether it's your first date with a woman or your five thousandth, the most important thing is to simply make an effort. Set the right mood and it won't matter if you're at a trendy French café or in the parking lot behind Hooters.

The following pages are packed with suggestions on creating that electric atmosphere in which sparks are born.

Don't have a date yet? We can help with that, too.

TOP TEN

Ways to Be a Gentleman

Okay, so there are precious few gents around. And not so many ladies. If she keeps her Womyn's Studies textbooks on the coffee table, these tips are sure to offend. But you never know when your favorite leather-babe might want to play the leading lady.

① Make the call. Don't leave the reservations up to your date. If you asked her out, that's your job. When you call ahead, ask for a quiet, candlelit table in the corner. And if you've never been to the restaurant before, ask about appropriate attire. All your slick, gentlemanly moves will lose their appeal fast if you're turned away at the door for not wearing a tie.

② Arrive armed. With a gift, that is. Greeting her at the door with flowers may seem clichéd to you, but won't to the woman you're trying to impress. Flowers are especially appropriate for a first date. Later on in your relationship, bring a bottle of wine for the two of you to share after your night out. Or surprise her by renting her favorite movie for a quiet night in.

③ Shield her. When walking with her on a city sidewalk, always position yourself between her and the street. This creates a barrier (you) between her and any dust, water, or catcalls created by passing motorists, plus it allows her to window-shop should the conversation hit a lull. Also, be conscious of your stride. Unless you're eating mammoth, you don't want to drag your woman to dinner.

④ Point out puddles. Keep your jacket on and walk *around* the darn thing. Your job is to spot it, not cover it.

⑤ Grab a revolver. You know about regular, hinged doors: They should be opened from the side and patiently held for an approaching woman. But a revolving door? You're the pusher. You go first.

6 **Unwrap her.** Remove a woman's wrap as if you were taking the plastic off a new TV—simply lift the covering off her shoulders. If it's a coat, lift up when she puts her arms down, and then slide the garment down and off.

7 **Sit her down.** Holding a chair for a lady is tricky. You don't want to be ostentatious. You want to be graceful. So do it this way: When she moves into position in front of the chair, carefully slide the chair in until the front edge of the seat is just about to touch the back of her legs. Once she sits down, then you can sit down. Don't drop your pencil and look up her skirt while picking it up. Expensive fountain pens are fine.

8 **Bring enough dough.** You pay. Period.

9 **Stand by.** When a woman leaves or approaches a crowded table, rise slightly from your chair. You don't want to actually point out that every other guy there is a manners moron. If it's just the two of you, then stand as if she were the national anthem. Just don't sing and then yell, "Play ball!"

10 **Walk her in.** Don't just drop her off at the door—unless you never want to go out with her again. Always get out and open the car door for her—then walk her to the front door. Even if she doesn't invite you in, the last thing she'll remember about your date is this gentlemanly gesture. And maybe she'll invite you in next time.

MUST READS

The Proposition

Asking a woman for a date is easy enough. Take deep breath. Blurt out request. Pray she doesn't run screaming. Giving her a reason to say yes—now that's a bit more challenging. In the dating game, women play defense. They take a moment to size you up and make a split-second decision. Are you an easy out or a home run? To score, you've got to make enough of an impression that she won't want to say no. Dr. Judy Kuriansky will show you how to be an All-Star date-getter in this excerpt from her book, The Complete Idiot's Guide to Dating *(Alpha Books, 1999).*

So you've spotted someone who strikes your fancy. Now it's time to take the next step: Make the connection. If you're stymied about what to do, you're certainly not alone. "How do I ask her out?" is a question I get asked all the time on my radio show. It seems so simple at first—just ask, right? Yet, why do you feel so nervous and anxious? Here you'll learn about what's cool and what's not when it comes to popping the question (not that question—we're working on the first date here).

What's New about Asking for the Date

Give up the old way of asking for the date—thinking of it as a "date!" Remember my basic principle: A date is an exciting invitation to spend time together. It's not about dating, it's about spending and enjoying time together and getting to know each other. So, what's the best way to do this?

Passé: Find the "right way."

In the New Millennium: There is no right way. Do what is natural for you, and remember to be yourself.

Passé: Make the invite "formal" (as in, "I'd like to ask you out" or "Do you want to go out on a date?").

In the New Millennium: Keep it casual. Think of a date as a time to hang out and get to know each other's likes and dislikes. This will help you feel less anxious.

Passé: Ask for a date far in advance in case she's busy or purposefully says "no" so you don't look desperate.

In the New Millennium: Ask when something comes up or the time feels right—it may be last minute, but asking spontaneously could be just what's appropriate. You can always apologize for asking at the last minute.

Passé: Ask if she is "free."

In the New Millennium: Assume she wants to go and then find out if the time is good for both of you. This concept allows you to approach the situation with self-confidence. If she is busy, you'll find out soon enough.

Passé: Don't call when you said you would.

In the New Millennium: Always call when you say you will; if you haven't said when, call (or e-mail) shortly after taking the phone number (even just to say hello).

Preliminaries . . .

Before asking someone out, brief yourself on the following dating tips to increase your chance of getting a "yes."

● Your invitation should not build anxiety for either of you. Wait for a moment when you feel relaxed.

● When asking someone on a date, consider what you enjoy doing. Participating in something you are good at or comfortable with will increase your overall confidence. If you like basketball, for example, take her to a game.

● Ask, "What's in it for my date?" As President John F. Kennedy said, "Ask not what your country can do for you; ask what you can do for your country." The same basic rule can be applied to dating: Always offer something to others before expecting or asking that something be done for you.

Think of a date not as getting,

SEX TRENDS

SEX AND THE (NEWLY) SINGLE GIRL

Disappointing news for the midlife crowd. It turns out that most divorced women are more like *Sex and the City*'s Miranda Hobbes than Samantha Jones.

"Contrary to popular belief, there isn't a big increase in the number of partners or frequency of sexual activity people have after they start or end a relationship," says John DeLamater, Ph.D., a sociologist at the University of Wisconsin at Madison. He surveyed 3,000 adults between the ages of 18 and 59 on their attitudes toward sex and the number of sexual partners and encounters they have each year.

His conclusions: Newly single adults are more wary about initiating sex with a new partner. Whether it's concern about disease, their own reputation, or something else, most recently separated people carry their values from marriage into the dating world, and are more monogamous than we'd expect.

but as giving. When inviting someone to a party, say, "There'll be some people there I know you'll enjoy." Or combat resistance by pointing out advantages, as in, "Come play golf with me. Even if you don't love the sport, you'll be outdoors getting sunshine and exercise, and seeing beautiful sights."

If a prospective date sees what she can get out of the evening, she will be more receptive. Also consider what she likes to do and how the date will benefit her. For example, if she is thinking of buying a new car, offer to spend a day visiting car showrooms.

● Remember the basic point: To be yourself, instead of feeling the pressure of what you're supposed to do, or even what the outcome will be.

● Face your fears about the ghosts of the past. A man named Sammy told me that he saw his kindergarten heartthrob at a reunion but was too scared to ask her out. He remembered the days as a youngster when he felt fat and awkward. With my encouragement, he called her—and was successful!

What Works?

Follow your instincts about what feels right for you. If you're going to be liked, you'll get a positive response no matter what you do. Therefore, you have some choices.

hot TIP!

Attracting women is easy, even if you don't play guitar. Just place a female friend at your elbow and tell a few jokes. Researchers at the University of Louisville found that a man was 50 to 100 percent more desirable to women when other ladies said they liked him. The best news: It didn't matter whether the man looked like George Clooney or George Costanza.

Whenever I pose the question on my radio show about the best ways to ask for a date, many male callers respond that they use the direct approach. As one caller named Mario said, "I just come right out and ask, 'How'd you like to go out?'" Another listener, Sean, agreed: "I'd be myself. I'd say, 'How'd you like to go out?'" Sammy, whom I described earlier, ended up using a very simple approach to ask out his kindergarten heartthrob: When he called her on the phone, he said, "Hey, how ya doin'?" Fortunately, she immediately recognized his voice and was enthusiastic, giving him the courage to ask, "What are you doing this weekend?" to which she replied, "My weekend's open . . ." He then said, "How about going out? We can get something to eat and go to a movie." She said she'd love to.

Personally, I favor the subtle approach. That

means you go with the flow when asking, making it a natural outgrowth of the interaction so that it doesn't seem like a formal invitation. The question shouldn't come out of nowhere. Ideally, you have both just finished discussing something in which you're both interested and that you would like to do together.

I am also in favor of starting the conversation with an offer. Think of entertaining the other person, offering her some tidbit of interesting information or a funny story rather than expecting her to carry the ball of the conversation. If the other person is the type who likes to entertain, you'll find that out soon enough. But if she isn't, then you've risked turning her off by putting her on the spot. I am more receptive to strangers when they approach me with a tidbit about why hurricanes take on a certain pattern than if they immediately ask, "Tell me what you do."

> " Where one goes wrong when looking for the ideal girl is making one's selection before walking the full length of the counter. "
>
> —P. G. Wodehouse

Use a technique similar to "free association," where topics lead into one another. Here's how the flow might go:

You could be talking about what you enjoy (playing baseball, for example). Then remind her about the amazing baseball players who broke the world's record for home runs (Mark McGwire and Sammy Sosa, who beat Roger Maris's 1961 record of 61 home runs) and ask what record she would like to break.

Suppose she answers that she doesn't know. Suggest records to break, like the number of hours dancing without stopping, and then segue into the suggestion that the two of you ought to go dancing sometime. Then swing into talking about how you heard the tango is a new craze, and that someday you'd like to visit Argentina. Then you can come back to the date—now that she's had a chance to let it sink in—saying how you love to dance and asking if she does. Move into another subject, picking up on the travel theme by talking about your last trip, and then come back to the invitation again. This time you're a little more definitive about whether you will get together: Say something like, "What do you think about going dancing next Friday?"

When and How?

Once you've decided you'll make a move, when's the right time to make it? Again, follow your instincts. Tune in to your own comfort level as well as hers.

Then strike when your iron is hot (when you feel motivated and empowered) and when your intuition tells you she would be receptive.

Asking in person has great advantages. Obviously, you can see the person's response (more about this later). However, you—and your prospective date—may feel put on the spot.

Short of that, the telephone also has advantages. You can get feedback from what you hear and listen for cues in the other person's voice. In addition, you won't be put on the spot—and if you get a "no," you can easily end the conversation.

Choose asking on the phone over other means (e-mail or voice mail). The latest craze, e-mail, is a great tool for shy people, but there really isn't any way for you to gauge your prospective date's response. Even if you have a solid e-mail relationship, pick up the phone and make your invitation. It's better if she hears your voice or better yet, sees your face in person.

Another new millennium mode: beeper and voice messages. The beeper has become like an answering machine, so you can consider beeping your prospective date. This has an element of surprise, but it's best to keep this method in reserve, to use in case you can't get in touch another way. If you leave a voice message, make it a vague "hello" and not the specific invitation. An exception to this: If you have last-minute tickets to some fabulous event and need an immediate answer. The element of excitement overrides any other caution about using this technique.

Closing the Deal

Asking someone on a date is like trying to make a sale—that is, you are trying to sell yourself. When making the proposition, follow the "Rule of Three Yesses": Ask three questions that will all lead to favorable responses. You never want to ask a question that will lead to a "no." That stops the conversation and injects negativity.

You also want to ease the person into agreement—without making her feel like she's risking too much or embarassing either of you—by giving her an out at each stage. Of course, you

hot **TIP!**

Never lose that phone number! You're sitting at a red light when the girl of your dreams pulls up alongside you and yells out her number. Then when the light turns green, she screeches away. By the time you find a pen, you can't be sure whether it was 737 or 773. Here's the solution: Rub your index finger against the side of your nose—it's always oily—and write each digit on your windshield. Later, just breathe on it to reveal the score.

have to do some research first and learn something about the person so that you can figure out how to set up your questions. Then you close the deal by asking three "yes" questions.

Consider this scenario: Bill wants to ask Kate out. He does a little research first and discovers that she likes Kung Fu movies. His conversation opener, therefore, can be: "I heard you like Kung Fu movies."

He then does more fact-finding by asking open-ended questions like, "What's the latest Kung Fu movie you've seen?" or "What's your favorite Kung Fu movie?"

Or, after a conversation about something else, Bill then can close the deal on his date by asking the following three "yes" questions:

perfect figures

WHY YOU SHOULD MOVE TO THE UNITED KINGDOM

Percentage of American women who admit to having premarital sex: 62

Percentage of British women who admit to having premarital sex: 98

. . . .

❶ "So, you really like going to the movies?"

❷ "I heard you love horror movies. Is that true?"

❸ "Wouldn't it be fun to see the latest horror movie playing at . . . ?"

Then Bill can add something along the lines of catching a movie the next weekend: "I'm thinking about going to see that movie sometime this weekend. Maybe you could go with me—what do you think?" (Of course, this won't always get you a definite yes, but you gave it a good shot.)

Notice these characteristics of Bill's invitation:

● Pose the question as if you're already going and she can join you. This takes the pressure off you to take her out formally and off her if she says no. You also avoid sounding desperate. (No one wants to board a sinking ship in full sail.)

● Be casual and light. Don't jump in to water that's too deep before you've tested it.

● Point out all the benefits of the deal. Folgers sells coffee not by quoting the price but by showing how warm and cozy consumers will feel sharing coffee with their spouse early in the morning.

How Persistent Should You Be?

A lot of people ask me how to tell whether someone is interested. Of course, you'd love an enthusiastic "Yes" when you ask her out, but my general rule is similar to baseball: three strikes and you're out. That means make three attempts but if you strike out those three times, back off and give up. Someone can turn you down two times for a legitimate reason. Maybe she's really busy or was a little ambivalent. Cut her a little slack. But after three approaches, take your time and energy elsewhere!

A man named Scott asked a girl he liked out and she said "no." Then he bumped in to her again, and she lit up, making him think she was interested. Scott took the bait, and called her up again. This time, she was warm, and even though she said she couldn't go, she said she'd love to do something another time. Maybe she was just being nice, but it was worth waiting a few weeks and then calling again. This time, she said yes. If she had been busy again, Scott could cross her off his list.

If the person really gives you encouragement and the excuses ring true, you can make an exception to the three-strikes rule. Her mother could be sick. She could be studying for the bar exam and not be able to spare the distraction. She could be breaking up with her boyfriend. But don't sit around and wait. Move on to other things—or other people. When the excuses are sincere, you'll go out eventually.

Getting the Number

So how do you get the phone number? You may be comfortable with being direct. Many of the male callers to my radio show have said they just come right out and ask, "Can I have your phone number?" Take Josh, for instance, who simply goes up to a lady and says "I'd like to have coffee with you sometime. What's your phone number?" He claims this has about a 60 percent success rate for him.

I favor a more subtle approach. Slide your request for the number into the conversation. While discussing something interesting, say something like, "Well, we should talk more about that." Then add, "How do we get in touch? I should give you my card/my number. And you should give me yours."

SEX TRENDS

WHY SHE CALLS EVERY HOUR

Researchers say that people dating someone new have brain patterns similar to those of people with obsessive-compulsive disorder.

Keeping Your Emotions in Check

When dating, it's important not to have any expectations. Enjoy the process and not the outcome, the journey and not the destination, or you'll be headed for disappointment. The best actions are the ones that come from the heart, that have good intentions and are not caught up with the actual "response." Have fun flirting without worrying whether it'll lead to a ride home, a date, a roll in the hay, or a marriage proposal. Your expectations may also make your date feel obligated, guilty, and resistant. People need to feel free to say yes or no instead of giving in because of guilt, fear of hurting you, fear of retaliation, or fear of anything else that can doom a relationship.

How to Pick the Perfect Partner

If you believe the skeptics, men and women are from different planets. Not in our universe, they aren't. Yeah sure, we need sex to feel close, and they need closeness to feel like sex. So what? We're still both earthbound and looking for a friend. As the parson said, that which unites us is greater than that which divides us. And guess what? We actually believe in the power of durable love. That's because we've read the studies about both coital frequency and life span—committed men get more and live longer, and that's especially true for married guys. Choose the right wife, and your future will be filled with unlimited sex, laughs, and companionship. Hugh O'Neill tells you how to pick the perfect partner.

I was about to undergo life-threatening surgery. Okay, it was a routine appendectomy. But sometimes anesthesiologists get to gabbing. And the surgical resident, doing his full-disclosure legal duty, did tell me that one possible side effect of the operation was death.

The hours before my surgery gave me plenty of time to get maudlin. I found myself goofy with gratitude—for world-class sisters and brothers, reasonable speed, some hand-eye coordination, healthy kids. But with an about-to-die clarity, I suddenly knew that my greatest blessing was, right now, standing in the doorway of my hospital room, asking the doctors to show her their licenses to practice in New Jersey. I knew, the way a dying man knows things, that my wife, Jody, was . . . well, let's say, in the top half of all the wives in the world.

In a flash, I saw a way to redeem a prodigal life. If I could help even one man find a wife like mine, I might yet leave a legacy. So, my hours dwindling down, I started scribbling wife-seeking wisdom on whatever shreds of hospital paper I could find.

Make no mistake, I don't claim to have made a wise wife choice. I stumbled onto a gold mine. I was 19, a morose, homesick college kid, carrying a tray through a dorm cafeteria when I heard Jody laugh, got a glimpse, and knew that I had to give this my best shot. She had obvious allures, but they were, I swear, beside the point. I didn't fix on her because she had a body by Botticelli and a smile like hope. I fixed on her because I fixed on her. Beginner's luck.

Connubial Cautions

For the mate seeker, these traits are yellow lights. Go slowly if she . . .

1 Believes in numerology
She thinks it's cosmic that you were born on the eighth day of the eighth month and she on the seventh day of the seventh.

2 Has a cat named Cleopatra
Be wary of this or any indication that she thinks she lived in Egypt in a past life.

3 Responds to your suggestion of snuggling with the question "Now?"
It's tough to say which is a worse wife omen: if she actually thinks you were proposing a quickie sometime next summer, or if she's just pretending to think that. The first means she has no clue about the male sex drive. The second means she does, but disapproves big-time.

4 Has more than one tattoo featuring a man's name
A "Stan" on her thigh you can live with. Hey, we were all young once. But if there's also a "Mack" on her lower back, keep looking.

5 Has even one tattoo featuring a woman's name

6 Redoes the dishes after you've done them
She may think of life as a mission to be accomplished, instead of a journey to be enjoyed.

7 Reminds you of your mother
If you ever find yourself thinking she moves like Mom or laughs like Mom or, worst of all, smells like Mom, move on.

The fact that I survived my brush with routine surgery should in no way diminish the advice. It is the wisdom of a man looking over the edge. I've consulted no "experts" on marriage. Instead I've consulted my memories of 28 years, two children, 10,000 laughs, and a handful of dark nights. Here are the rules for picking the perfect partner, for making the most important choice of your life.

First, a Few Things That Don't Matter

The three things most often cherished in a wife-to-be are (1) beauty, (2) brains, and (3) common interests.

Wrong, wrong, and it's debatable.

● Looks don't matter.

Take it easy. I'm not saying you have to spend a lifetime looking across the table at a nice personality. Your wife should float your boat. But beware the beauty trap. It can short-circuit the sweetheart search.

You know that idealized, hourglass, Halle Berry image of beauty with which the sexist, patriarchal power structure has tried to diminish regular women? Well, it's bad news for women, but it's even worse for men. We've swallowed our sales pitch. We're so attuned to this narrow band of beauty, we're often deaf to signals from outside the frequency.

We're way too finicky at the female feast. We rule out women as potential partners for dozens of dumb anatomical reasons: too short, too tall, too thin-lipped, too wide-hipped, too this, not enough that. Every day, men cruise past the answer to their prayers because she comes in an original package. Remember, plenty of GMs passed on Montana out of Notre Dame because he didn't look like a quarterback. At crunch time, a trophy is just baggage; you want a player.

Almost all women are attractive to marry. Not many are hot enough to be your date at the Golden Globes, but marriage isn't a beauty pageant. This is your life we're talking about. Get susceptible. Find more women attractive, pal. They all are.

● Brains don't matter.

More precisely, virtually everybody has enough of them to be a good spouse. Sure, the world has its geniuses and its dolts, but 90 percent of us fall somewhere in the perfectly functional middle. It's important that there be some rough parity when it comes to brains. If she's a lot dumber than you are, you'll get bored. Worse, if she's a lot smarter, she will. Note: This has nothing to do with educational level, but rather with how quickly and well a person's brain works. Here's a useful test:

When the first volley in an argument is fired, there should be no clear bet-ting favorite. If you can handle her with one quip tied behind your back, it's unlikely this match will have the risk to keep it dynamic.

● **Common interests may not matter.**
Sometimes wildly diverse interests may be a better bet. Keep in mind: One of the big threats to wedded bliss is centripetal force, the tendency for a marriage to collapse in on itself. If both peas are from the same pod, it can get claustrophobic in there.

If you're both survivalists from the Sawtooth Range, swapping stories of stockpiling canned goods can grow a tad tiresome. But if you're a sunny, big-government liberal, you may be a nice complement to her cataclysmic bent. If you hear the trumpets and she hears the strings, there may just be a symphony between you. Any two human beings have all they need in common. Growing up in Massapequa or Minsk is of no moment.

Nine Things That Matter a Lot
Poker players would call these "tells," signs that she could be a sterling spouse:

❶ She should be tender.
A wife should be willing to kiss it where it hurts. Why? Because grown men, they do get weary. There are bumps in the road out there. Sure, your plan is that you'll take care of her. But at some point, you're going to need some consolation. Does the word "downsizing" mean anything to you?

Beware the conservative Republican, especially if her issue of choice is over-

hot **TIP!**

You've been single since you can remember and you're wondering why it is that the women on Sex and the City *are so, well . . . sexed, and all the women you meet seem to have lost their sex drive. We decided to send a group of undercover researchers to find out just where to meet the girls that could spice up your life. Here are five places they discovered where you can meet women without looking obvious or catching a disease.*

1. The grocery store
Best time: Right after work
Tip: Look for women who are buying for one

2. Bookstores
Best time: Evenings
Tip: Avoid women browsing in the self-help section

3. The gym
Best time: Either before or after work
Tip: Don't approach her while she's sweating

4. The video store
Best time: Around eight
Tip: Just check she's not renting *Fatal Attraction*

5. Night classes
Best time: No time like the present, man
Tip: Study a language—the sexiest women learn languages

hauling the welfare system, taking those deadbeats off the dole. You want a wife whose first instinct is caretaking. Sexist? Yes. Doesn't matter. Down the road, when you're tired, you'll want a softie, a mushball who cries at treacly movies, who wants everybody to feel all right and thinks maybe she can help.

② She should be properly respectful of sports.

A wife need not like sports—at all. But neither should she be hostile to the contests. Here's a wonderful wife indicator.

perfect figures

WHY YOU SHOULD READ THIS SECTION EVEN IF YOU'RE MARRIED

Percentage of marriages that break up within the first 15 years: 43

You're in front of the tube. Miami-Jets. Playoffs. It's snowing at the Meadowlands. The spirits of Marino and Joe Willie are hovering over the red zones. Suddenly, unsolicited, she sashays in, puts some snacks on the coffee table, kisses the top of your head, and beats a retreat. Granted, the unprovoked delivery of snack food plays to serving-wench fantasies. But that's a trivial extra, compared with the bigger truth it reveals about this woman. Unlike the sarcastic woman (the one who sees you splayed out on the couch and says, "Oh, are the pituitary boys knocking each other down again?"), the wench . . . uh, pretzel-bringer understands your need to symbolically indulge the kaboom that is, through no fault of yours, encoded on your Y chromosome. She knows that when an intruder breaks in and you head downstairs to check it out, she'll be mighty glad you spent those hours with Madden and Summerall, instead of sussing out stemware at Pottery Barn.

③ She should be Velcro.

Our official position is that men don't need civilizing. But the truth is that a lot of us are still cowboys—almost alone on the range. We still don't understand that the phone can be used for gabbing with your sister, not just calling 911. Your wife is going to be your link to the rest of the world. So she should be a sticky person.

You want a woman who's good at staying in touch, whose phone rings a lot. She should be enthusiastic about people, love them—now get this—in spite of how odd and difficult they are. Keep in mind, she's going to be the kids' mother. If you want to get the most out of family life, she should be a reacher-outer who likes to talk and is skilled on the phone. Think very carefully before you marry a woman who has no girlfriends. You want a wife who enjoys the human campfire. You've got the antisocial urge covered.

She should be a memory nut, too. Try to find a woman who's ardent about experiences for no other reason than that the two of you had them together. Believe it or not, it's a good sign that she likes to relive that nothing-much dinner in that Italian restaurant. She's gathering the threads of your story, weaving them into a blanket that will eventually keep you warm. The ultimate wife sees the two of you as a great legend, like Burns and Allen.

Why Would She Marry You?

Okay, she's got all nine wife traits and is a babe to boot. But that doesn't mean she'll say "yes" to your best offer. We asked the womenfolk for specs they seek in a spouse.

● Some reasonable job history
She'll probably pass on your proposal if more than 40 percent of your income over the past 5 years comes from severance packages.

● A telephone
Women dig outlaws for short-term thrills, but for the long-term deal, they get cautious if you "don't really need a phone." If you're estranged from your family, it may mean you won't care for hers, either. Actually caring about other human beings is a husband green light.

● A powerful genetic package
Since "husband" usually means "Daddy," women assess the DNA you bring to the deal. But they have only a passing interest in broad shoulders or soulful eyes; they're looking for the genes for affection, patience, and piggyback rides. Indif-

ference to her adorable nephew could hurt your chances.

● Some shred of sensitivity
Women prefer husbands who are made of flesh and blood to the stone variety. Make no mistake: There will be no crying—unless there's a death, a serious illness, or a catastrophic margin call. But you should feel free to offer that you thought *Lethal Weapon 3* was the most poignant of the Gibson-Glover series. The sensitivity thing is tricky, because they're also looking for . . .

● . . . An I-beam at the core
Women look for a good man in a storm. Underneath that amiable exterior, they want steel. Be sensitive, but not so sensitive you can't still be her rock.

● . . . Ears
Women are crazy for good listeners. If

④ She should be loyal.

Test: You utter a mild criticism of her drug-dealer brother. She should leap immediately to his defense. People don't stand up for each other much these days. Loyalty will come in handy, especially when you're the guy who needs a champion.

⑤ She should be able to process all the health-insurance forms.

No family can survive financially without somebody who has this ability. Since most men don't have the patience to do it, look for a partner who does. By the way, if you can deal with these forms, don't take a woman who can do it, too. In our opinion, this ability is too precious to be duplicated in one family.

⑥ She should have a low pleasure threshold.

This has nothing to do with sex—though, come to think of it, being erotically easy may be a boon, too. A good partner has a weakness for small delights.

you can repeat something she said last week, she'll probably marry you.

● . . . An animal on a leash

Most women don't mind a trace of the primitive, as in a now-and-then glance at Miss Britney on VH-1. But they get skittish if your inner animal is in charge. No kissing the screen when Ms. Spears appears. No togas. No road trips.

Also avoid these less-than-engaging moves:

● Wearing your Miami Heat tank top to meet her parents

● Christening your big toenail ("All hail the Saber, baby!")

● Calling children *tar maggots*

● Using the phrase *Who's your Daddy?*

● Or commenting, "Interestingly, most societies aren't monogamous."

Let the word go forth from this time and place: Domestic life is not all shivers and champagne. There are moments, days, even weeks, when all you do is go back and forth to work, make the kids dinner, do some laundry, and then do laundry again. You want a wife who can spin this stuff into gold. A taste for tiny joys may be the most valuable mate trait there is.

In truth, plain old everyday life is deep and rich, full of elations that too often go unnoticed. A partner who can, without speeches about sunsets, point you to modest glories is golden. Look for a woman who works up close, who's sappy about small attentions, who savors a morning cup of coffee, a sitcom enjoyed side by side, a new lawn sprinkler, the light on a late-summer afternoon. Look for sweet energy, brought to bear quietly throughout the day.

Value the "v" virtues (verve, vitality, vigor) and the "z" word (zest) as well.

❼ She should bust you.

You don't want a wife who's an easy sell. Remember Hepburn and Tracy in all those old rat-a-tat-tat movies? They were always teasing each other, testing each other, goading each other. You want a wife who is feisty, who gives you an affectionate hard time.

This is a tennis match. No fun in an opponent who can't return the ball. Your spouse is a whetstone against whom you sharpen your instrument. It took Hagler to bring out the best in Sugar Ray.

❽ She should be good at intimacy.

How often does she whisper? The more the better. And how often does she look at you as though there is no rest-of-the-world, as though you and she are a universe of two? Also, the more, the better.

❾ She should be part tortoise and part hare.

Stop any physiologist in a parking lot and he'll tell you that people have two kinds of muscle fibers—the fast-twitch fire quickly; the slow-twitch have a longer fuse. Though everybody has some of each, sprinters feature rapid-fire; marathoners are long on slow. Life is both a sprint and a marathon. The ideal wife is a hybrid, equal parts Marion Jones and Greta Waitz.

She's got the sass for a dash and the will to conquer Heartbreak Hill. She can use energy both in short bursts and in a slow burn across the years.

Favor the energetic. Seek out an inclination to laughter and a gift for hope. By this sign shall you know her. When she walks into the room, you'll feel two exactly opposite reactions: (1) ever-so-slightly pepped up, as though the starter's gun might sound any sec, and (2) surpassingly calm, as though there will be time enough for everything.

THE FUNNY PAGE

*"I had a nice time, Steve. Would you like to come
in, settle down, and raise a family?"*

HELP ONLINE

DATING BASICS

Whether you're just getting back in the saddle or you're a true dating
ignoramus, this site offers the candid advice you'll need to get a date,
and possibly score. Get your questions answered, read about
dating disasters you'll want to avoid, or plan the perfect date—all with
the help of the site's concierge. With a name like Demetre, he's gotta
know something about women's tastes.
www.dating911.com

MEET YOUR MATCH

Looking for love? This site boasts a list of 3 million members
with 8,000 more joining each day. Browse for babes or
post info about yourself at no charge. You only have to ante up
if you'd like to contact someone you meet on the site. Then you
have a choice of a 1-month, 6-month, or 1-year subscription.
www.americansingles.com

FIND MS. RIGHT

Got a bazillion ex-girlfriends? Here's how to make them work for you.
Plug in what you liked most and least about your exes and how
happy each date made you. This site will then spit out a description of the
ideal mate for you. Now if only it could only spit out a real girlfriend.
www.netstorm.net/~mauldin/dpa/dpaform.html

Rules Women and Code Men: Game-Playing Beauties versus Sex-Obsessed Beasts?

An Interview with Lawrence LaRose

Once upon a time (well, in early 1996), two women named Ellen Fein and Sherrie Schneider wrote a book for women about how to get a husband. They called it The Rules: Time-Tested Secrets for Capturing the Heart of Mr. Right. *Their rules essentially told women to play hard to get. They got a mixed reception from women as well as men—some called the tips "effective screening," while others called them "manipulation."*

Later that same year, two men named Nate Penn and Lawrence LaRose wrote a Rules *rebuttal, calling it* The Code: Time-Tested Secrets for Getting What You Want from Women without Marrying Them!

Both books became top sellers, leaving us to wonder if people were actually applying their principles to real life and expecting to live happily ever after. The books are so different—one cannot help but see them as the Foreman-Ali match of the sex wars—that we figured the two genders would have stopped talking to each other by now.

Since most of the men and women we know seem to get along (in the office anyway) we thought the rules/code issue would be worth another look.

Now, we could have talked to the rules girls, but we knew they would say a whole bunch of stuff men would rather not hear. So we opted for guy talk instead and spent some time with The Code *co-author Lawrence LaRose. He told us that, in the world of dating, you'd be surprised who prevails.*

MAN'S GUIDE: It's been 6 years since you and Nate published *The Code*, which was, of course, pretty much a response to *The Rules*. Now that more than a half-decade has come and gone, do they even think of that book anymore, or have they driven the horrid memories from their minds?

> **LAROSE:** Well, I don't know about all other guys, but I don't *want* to completely forget that book. I've always thought of *The Rules* as a great book of sociology. Those women were able to capture exactly the way women treat men . . . in high school! The game playing, the manipulation—it's almost too heady in its nostalgia to contemplate.

Besides, how can we forget completely? The authors are still in the news from time to time. Heck, males across the country got the news not so long ago that one of *The Rules* "girls," Ellen Fein, is getting divorced. The upside of that is that we can still lust after them vigorously—well, the divorced one anyway—and call one or both of them up for a date.

On second thought, there's one big downside: They're both shrill. And I am very happily married now. Damn, that's two.

Still, maybe some other guy can get a date with Ellen and see if the strategies in *The Code* can undermine her commitment to *The Rules*.

MAN'S GUIDE: Men don't like to dwell on the unpleasant side of wooing women, so I imagine a lot of men *have* forgotten *The Rules*. Have women forgotten? Or is that too much to hope for?

LAROSE: It doesn't really matter if women forget the book. It won't help the men much even if they do. The "rules" have always been around: Play at being meek, don't be too forthcoming, let the men pretend to call the shots. This needs a book?

MAN'S GUIDE: Okay, so the basic rules of the game remain the same. Has the dating landscape changed much in the years since both *The Rules* and *The Code* hit the shelves?

LAROSE: Well, of course, I got married in September 2000—that might be a hypocritical sign to some, but hell, I can't peddle snarky little paperbacks my whole life. It was time to settle down and set a good example for Senator Condit.

MAN'S GUIDE: There's some kind of irony there: A rules gal gets divorced; a code guy gives in to marriage. It would have made for great press coverage if you had hooked up with each other.

LAROSE: Hook up? I'm getting hot flashes just thinking about that. Maybe the lesson from the past 5 years—as well as from Ricki Lake or Jerry Springer—is that no matter how dysfunctional you are in your dating life, you will always be outclassed by some other ménage of lunatics on one of those programs.

In other good news, we have that great relationship "documentary" *Sex and the City* on HBO. I'm sure that's influenced dating somehow. Now all the women are getting advice from that show on everything from how to deal with lunatics on dates to how to say goodbye to a guy. And for the men, we get a great bird's-eye view of what women are thinking.

MAN'S GUIDE: How has *The Rules* changed the dating landscape, the prospect of getting married, etcetera?

> **LAROSE:** Unless someone can point to an incidence of a copy of *The Rules* spontaneously propagating human life, thus adding to the pool of people eligible to get married, I'd say not one whit. There's a heightened and jokey sense of who makes the first phone call. And there's a new vocabulary in the dating world—terms like *rules girls*— but it's more like some demonic Esperanto version of the old lingo. Nothing substantive has changed due to that book.

MAN'S GUIDE: How has *The Code* changed any of those things?

> **LAROSE:** Again, not one whit. Men still love sex. Women still love shoes. *The Code* may have played a part in loosening up—if I can use that term—sexual discussion. And the wave of not-quite-gutsy-enough-to-be-pornographic men's magazines like *Maxim* has certainly added to the sense that we men can pursue more "laddish" behavior. But has the book really changed anything? Naw, the laws of thermodynamics still hold. It was a send-up; it wasn't meant to change the world.

MAN'S GUIDE: What would be the "new millennium" response to *The Rules*?

> **LAROSE:** With the impending divorce of one of the rules girls, why does anyone need to respond? They have become a parody of them-selves. They pretended to have all the answers, yet they fare no better than the general populace with its 50-percent divorce rate.

MAN'S GUIDE: Should there be a new response to *The Code*?

> **LAROSE:** Like the authors of *The Rules*, I'm now a mockery of my-self—though to be honest, I never took my book as seriously as they took theirs. But still, here I co-wrote a book on being an unapologetic bachelor, and now I am happily married to a wonderful woman. I'm

sorry, guys, but I couldn't help myself. She was too good to pass up . . . and she's holding a gun to my head.

MAN'S GUIDE: I am going to assume that your wife was not a rules girl.

LAROSE: No, she was not—and is not. She is far from a "surrendered wife" type. She's not one of those meek "I'll wait until you call me" kind of women.

MAN'S GUIDE: Now that you're married, do you miss the dating world at all, or are you glad to be rid of it and settled in a good relationship?

LAROSE: There's a sense of relief to be out of it. I have a certain respect for the dating world, its rigors, and the people who can navigate that territory comfortably. And dating can be a lot of fun. At the same time, though, I wonder about the sanity of people who choose to— and desire to—remain in that world for their entire lives. It seems like people who do that are setting themselves up for a lifetime of elevated expectations and serious letdowns.

Still, despite the fun that can be had simply dating, it's a terrible, deranged system. Unfortunately, it's the best system we have for getting men and women together. Even more unfortunate, the system is getting worse and more dreary, I think.

It's hard to point your finger at a single thing that is making it worse, but I think a lot of it has to do with [our] suspicion of others and our increasing reliance on forms of telecommunications that put us . . . out of touch with people on a personal basis. It's hard to meet people casually anymore and just have fun. Everyone is too busy with work or whatever else, or seems to have a hidden motive.

MAN'S GUIDE: Awfully deep stuff, there.

LAROSE: Well, it's unfortunately true, and I have to acknowledge it. You often don't know who people are anymore. It's either a facade in a bar or a pimply 13-year-old kid online pretending to be someone else. And a lot of people just don't have the time—or they refuse to make the time—to get past the surface and the illusions.

Not that fantasy isn't a great thing. People loved watching *Temp-*

tation Island in part because participants were allowed to date and have rampant fun. But you cannot just throw your arm around some woman in the real world. That's called harassment. Heck, you're lucky if you can compliment a woman at work without getting in trouble. Cynicism is at high tide now.

MAN'S GUIDE: So what's the answer?

LAROSE: Well, *The Rules* certainly isn't the answer. The whole "rules" notion kind of feeds into this culture of cynicism and mistrust and game playing.

Part of the reason Nate and I wrote *The Code* was to sort of say, "Lighten up." Much of the jokiness of *The Code* was done in the hope that people would drop the facades, put their cynicism slightly in check, and have fun—laugh at themselves and just enjoy each other.

One of the terrible things about *The Rules* and a lot of things in the dating scene is that people don't want to let their guards down, and they don't want to "settle" for someone until they find that perfect person. What they don't realize is that if you are looking for perfection, you will likely be looking forever.

MAN'S GUIDE: Did you and Nate intend for *The Code* to provide any serious dating advice?

LAROSE: Basically, *The Rules* was every man's worst nightmare: A woman only wants to have sex so that you will marry her. *The Code* responded with a woman's worst nightmare: A man will only talk about marriage so he can get sex. Even Bill "Code" Clinton was pushed into this sort of talk, with Monica "Rules" Lewinsky actually bringing up the happily ever after with him at some point.

Anyway, in terms of seriousness, there are certainly some truths lurking in between the humor and sarcasm of our book. If you read the chapter The Person with the Most Problems Controls the Relationship, you might think of some of your relationships and think, "Yeah, I was a nutcase—and in total control!"

The Code was also a send-up of self-help books in general, spoofing the idea that you could find romantic happiness within the confines of a flimsy paperback. Hell, if you were really able to "help" your "self," why would you need a book to do it?

The point is—and this is not ever clearly or sincerely stated in *The Code*—that good relationships are about communication, not manipulation. It's simple to say but difficult to achieve without really expensive medications and comfy pillows.

MAN'S GUIDE: Is there anything that you look at in *The Rules* and say, "Darn, the women were right on that point?"

LAROSE: Not from the book so much. But damn, did they know how to self-promote. I certainly learned that from them. Nate and I were on Oprah's show with one of *The Rules* girls and, boy, could she talk. We just got slaughtered by her fusillade of self-promotion. Someone would pause—just leave open the barest sliver of airtime— and she would jump in and tear through time like a chain saw.

That was pretty impressive. After she stopped talking, I could swear I had abrasions. Which, I guess, kind of flew in the face of their own advice to let the man talk first. Maybe if we had been on a date she would have let me speak.

MAN'S GUIDE: Is there anything in *The Code* that you look back on and say, "Whoops?"

LAROSE: One of the most popular chapters in *The Code* was also the shortest: How to Meet the Parents . . . Don't. Now I look back on that with an experienced eye and say, "Damn straight."

But really, that's a lie too. My in-laws are just as nutty as any other set of parents, of course, but they are also supremely warm and fantastic people.

MAN'S GUIDE: When you set these two books side by side, is there any sign of common ground between the sexes, aside from sexual anatomy that fits together nicely?

LAROSE: In a word, malaise. Misery. Unhappiness. Oops, I guess that's three words.

Men and women are unhappy with the dating landscape today. "All the good men are taken," say the women. For their part, the men cannot help but notice that all the good women are with Russell Crowe.

We work too hard, and we have too little time. So dating itself becomes work, with fewer and fewer benefits—and no 401(k) plan. In both books, I think if you dig deep, you will find a ray of hope. Mind you, it will have to be really, really deep in the case of *The Rules*. But if you dig down, you will see that both books do exhibit a desire to, at some point in life, do away with the game-playing and charades.

MAN'S GUIDE: What is the single biggest thing men and women refuse to see eye to eye on?

LAROSE: Refrigerators.

MAN'S GUIDE: That's so Zen I'm not even going to ruin it by asking what it means.

LAROSE: That's just as well.

MAN'S GUIDE: Anyway, we've talked generalities, so we'll throw a specific at you—a real-world example we've seen happen to a lot of friends over the years.

Why the heck is it that if you're a man who is close friends with a woman—or, rather, lusting after her but not able to make the connection—why is it that she will cry on your shoulder, share her deepest fears with you, give you the "Let's be friends" speech, yet follow that up with a quick full-mouth kiss or a desire to cuddle up with you nonsexually in bed on a semi-regular basis?

LAROSE: There's an air of complaint in the question. What's the problem? If you don't know how to convert her, my friend, I suggest you get a self-help book, one called *The Code*. That's C-O-D-E.

MAN'S GUIDE: You really did learn a lot about shameless self-promotion from the authors of *The Rules*, Lawrence. We commend you.

LAROSE: Thanks.

MAN'S GUIDE: Seriously, though, this isn't the "hypothetical friend" thing. Do women know they are giving men these terrible mixed signals when they befriend and even date them? Do they care? Is this some kind of rules thing?

> **LAROSE:** You mean, is the whole "push me/pull you" thing intentional?

MAN'S GUIDE: Yeah. That's one of the big mysteries we've always wondered about.

> **LAROSE:** I don't know if it's conscious. It's like the person who will pass up the third parking space down the row to look for something closer to the front door of the store. It's as if women think about guys in this way and decide, "You're great, but what if Ron Perlman is about to be smitten with me?" Or, "You're a wonderful match for me, but hey, David Duchovny might be just waiting around the corner." It's like insurance.

MAN'S GUIDE: So the woman hedges her bets by keeping a guy on the hook just enough to make sure she can fall back on him if nothing better pans out.

> **LAROSE:** Sure. It may not be the most pleasant thing in the world, but the woman figures she needs to keep her options open. People hate insurance, but it doesn't stop them from buying it or using it.

MAN'S GUIDE: One last question, and the subtitle of your book really begs that this be asked: Is it *really* possible for an average guy to get what he wants from a woman in terms of a casual relationship over a really long span of time—without ever having to marry her?

For that matter, looking at it from the *Rules* side, is it really possible for an average woman to land the guy she wants without eventually putting out?

And if so, is either of those options something men or women should be proud of?

All right, we lied; that's three questions.

> **LAROSE:** When the people of the world finally come to their senses and start giving out Nobel prizes for nookie, the person who can answer those questions will win the first one. On the other hand, Stedman Graham has been dating Oprah Winfrey for years without getting married. Either he's got the answer or she's not putting out!

QUICKIES

SHE LIKES IT LOUD

The best destination for a first date may be a concert. Or, if you're a cheapskate, a record store with listening stations. Researchers found that playing music above 90 decibels—the typical audio level at a rock concert or dance club—generated pleasurable sensations among listeners. The saccule, a tiny chamber in the inner ear that may control cravings for sex, vibrated when subjects listened to loud music. Despite their startling discovery, the researchers still didn't get lucky.

MYTH: MEN ALWAYS MAKE THE FIRST MOVE

The truth: Actually, we're just kidding ourselves. "Women avidly court men using facial gestures, seductive glances, touching, and provocative dress to let men know they're available," says anthropologist Helen Fisher, Ph.D., from Rutgers University in New Brunswick, New Jersey. We may think we're always initiating contact, but much of the time we're instinctively reacting to signals transmitted to us by women. (Our parents called it flirting.)

> **" My love life is a never-ending ribbon of what-ifs. I suspect every man's is. "**
>
> —author Joe Kita on remembering the girl who got away, in his book *Another Shot: How I Relived My Life in Less Than a Year* (Rodale, 2001).

READ HER LAUGH LINES

We never know how we're doing when it comes to talking to a potential mate. Just when we think we're in, we're out. And when we think there's no way, we discover that all the while she was interested. So, finally, here's a foolproof method to ensure that if you do go home alone, it's because you deserve to.

An Australian study has shown that crow's feet—those creases that appear when we laugh—are natural signs that we analyze to determine whether or not someone likes us.

Using infrared sight trackers, psychologists from Sydney University found that we subconsciously look at these laugh-lines to tell us how genuine a person is. Apparently false smiles don't display as many creases. So next time you're talking with a woman, look for lines to see if she's interested and sincere.

Q: *My girlfriend and I are in a long-distance relationship. Lately, whenever we get together, I've noticed that while I'm in a hurry to have sex, she isn't. In fact, sometimes we don't even have sex for several days, even when we haven't seen each other for a long time.* <u>*Is this a sign that something's wrong with our relationship, or that she's no longer attracted to me?*</u>
—M. L., Birmingham, Alabama

A: Sex is a barometer for the status of any relationship. If the frequency with which a couple is having sex begins to decline very rapidly over a short period of time, that's a sign that something's most likely wrong in the relationship.

Before you panic, clarify your expectations for sex. Is your partner looking for warmth and social support? Or maybe sex just isn't as important to her as it is to you. You shouldn't expect your girlfriend to rush off a plane and immediately want to take you to a hotel room. However, she also shouldn't spend an entire weekend with you without becoming intimate or affectionate in some way.

Next, if things between the two of you have changed unexpectedly over a short period of time, look for crises that may be going on in her life. When she's stressed and upset about something, it's likely that your sex life may suffer slightly until that issue is resolved.

If you still can't find the problem, gently confront her about it. Try not to be defensive or offensive when you bring the issue up. Sit down with her, hold her hand, and tell her you haven't been paying enough attention to her, and that you want to know how she's doing.

If she still won't open up to you, it could be a sign she wants to break things off and hasn't worked up to it yet.

Q: *I'm back in the dating scene after being married for 14 years.* <u>*What do I need to know about STDs?*</u>
—M. W., New York City

A: There's no question that the post-divorce freedom to pursue women who were once off-limits can be liberating. But you're right to pursue this freedom cautiously. A growing number of men are finding it can turn on them when they least expect it—leaving them to contend with issues they may never have faced before, like sexually transmitted diseases.

The problem is that middle-aged men grew up before the era of sex education. When they re-enter the dating pool after divorce and failed relationships, they aren't protecting themselves or practicing safe sex the way younger men learned to as part of growing up.

Here are some good rules to follow.

perfect figures

HMM. AND WHAT PERCENTAGE OF AMERICA IS FEMALE?

Number of Americans who believe in love at first sight: 52

Of those, percentage who say they have experienced it: 69

- Get a hepatitis B vaccination several months before you begin dating again.

- Don't brush or floss right before kissing. Microtears in the gums from either activity can increase your risk of infections.

- Ask her what diseases she's been tested for. Volunteer your own information. It may be awkward, but it could also save your life.

- Avoid sex with people who have warts or sores around the genitals, discoloration of the genitals, or rashes or outbreaks in the region—all are possible symptoms of infection.

- Wear a condom with your partner, or use some sort of protective layer, for at least the first six months of your relationship. If condoms are uncomfortable for you, or you don't get maximum stimulation while wearing one, try dripping some lubricant inside the condom before putting it on.

The Sex Doc is a fictional character.
The actual advice was provided by a variety of
medical doctors and other qualified experts.

6

SEX
IN THE
PUBLIC EYE

 Nobody enjoys a sex scandal quite the way we Americans do. While other countries are content to quietly sweep their politicians' indiscretions under the carpet, we can't help but make a lot of noise. Mayor flaunts a new girlfriend? Civil-rights leader fathers an illegitimate child? We'll air constant updates on cable news and run endless stale jokes on late-night TV.

Why so much fascination with other people's sex lives? We have a theory: Under that buttoned-down façade of modesty, we're all either slobbering voyeurs or shameless exhibitionists. Some of us are both.

It's nothing to be ashamed of. Heck, it's wired into our brains. Embrace it. Have sex in a national park. Walk around naked in your living room. Tune in to the dirty movies they play at 1:00 A.M. It won't hurt anybody. Just don't blame us if you end up on the 11-o'clock news.

Tricks from Skin Flicks

We're not huge fans of adult movies—unless of course you can learn something from them. Then we're all for them. That's why we sent one of our writers home with 40 X-rated videos. When he emerged 3 days later, broken and empty, he was still conscious enough to bring us these lessons for the bedroom.

① Don't finish where you started. Three minutes is about as long as you'll see any two (or more) actors in the same sexual position; they'll reconfigure several times during a scene to keep things interesting. You should, too. It can keep you from ejaculating too soon.

② Use your head. To keep your tongue from getting tired during oral sex, try sticking it out, closing your mouth around it, and moving your entire head. You'll last twice as long.

③ Stretch out. Have her lie flat on her back with her legs straight up in the air and her knees together. Kneel facing her, with your legs spread wide on the bed. Enter her with her feet resting over your shoulders. The advantage: You'll get deep, tight penetration without too much contortion.

④ Thrust one at a time. Penetrate slowly, then withdraw completely; wait a second and start over, 10 times. "Insertion is everyone's favorite part of intercourse," says Mark Elliott, Ph.D., a sex therapist. (Okay, maybe second favorite.) Repeating the initial insertion will help you savor the feeling. Be careful; you could like it so much that you finish before you're ready.

⑤ Bounce. If she's on top, have her sit still so you can do the bouncing—and control the speed of the friction. Bend your knees and use your thigh muscles. When you move up and down, you'll slide in and out. Stay in control so she doesn't slide all the way off.

6 **Touch and tease.** For a different sensation, use two fingers to stroke up and down: This stimulates both sides of her clitoris without actually touching it.

7 **Use her legs.** Have her lie on her back with one leg straight; the other leg should be pulled in toward her chest. Straddle her straight leg and support yourself with an arm hooked into the crook of her bent knee. "This allows good access, but because her legs are still together, she'll get lots of clitoral stimulation," says Elliott. That's a good thing.

8 **Stay clothed.** Usually, you get naked, then you have sex. Next time, try giving her oral sex through her panties. She'll like the way the damp cotton feels against her.

9 **Stop worrying about aim.** You know her clitoris needs attention, especially as she nears climax. But it's hard to find such a tiny target when both your bodies are moving. Use the flat of your palm to make broad, quick circular motions around the front of her vaginal opening. That way, you're sure to hit the spot.

10 **Play the part.** Let go of all your inhibitions and pretend you're making your own porn flick. You're the stable boy seduced by an oil baron's daughter. Or a mob boss having a fling with cousin Joey's supermodel wife. Or get really crazy and switch roles with her. (Ever watch *Bend Over Boyfriend*?)

MUST READS

Best Sex Spots

Technically speaking, you can have sex anywhere. No site requirements or building permits necessary. No need to take a survey or do an environmental-impact study. Furniture? Optional. Really, you need no other equipment—at least no equipment you're not already carrying around. Yet 99 times out of 100 you do it in a room and on an object specifically meant for, of all things, sleeping. No wonder it gets boring. Here Ted Spiker awakens you to a whole new world of airplane lavatories, fitness equipment, household appliances, even subterranean caves. We guarantee you'll never look at the world the same way again.

If men weren't great explorers, we never would have found America, the Rockies, or scrambled porn on channel 99. So why should our entire sex lives always take place in the same spots? Nothing against the 5-foot-by-7-foot package of coiled springs you'll be bouncing on tonight, but we believe every man should act on his inherent urge to conquer new territory. The benefit: A sex life with more imagination is one with more satisfaction. So here's our list of the world's 34 best places to fool around. Try some of our suggestions (discreetly, please; bail isn't in our budget). Or just use them as inspiration to make a list of your own.

❂ Airline
There's no need to try cramped bathroom sex when you're flying business class on British Airways. Some planes feature "fully flat bed" seats—which, as promised in the promotional material, will "allow you to get completely horizontal." The seats are arranged in pairs with one person's head at another person's feet. (Could this get any better?) Eventually, the seats will be available in the entire fleet, but they're currently only on planes that fly New York routes. For reservations, call (800) 247-9297 or see www.britishairways. com. Please use the privacy screen.

❂ Fitness equipment
Although we can think of several hundred kinky things to do with a calf-raise machine, our vote for most sexual piece of fitness equipment is a large Swiss ball. Why? The ball can actually help improve your depth of penetration, if you're in the right position. Try this: Sit on the ball and have her straddle you, facing away from you. Hold her hips for balance, and use the rocking motion of the ball to thrust in and out of her from behind. Do one set of at least 50 repetitions. Be courteous: Wipe off the ball when you finish your set.

● Hotel

Spare yourself the embarrassment of shopping downtown for leather chaps and cheerleader outfits. Just fulfill all of your fantasies at the Madonna Inn in San Luis Obispo, California. Each of the 109 rooms is designed with a different tacky theme. There's the romantic (the Anniversary Room), the exotic (the Safari Room), and the whimsical (the Caveman Room, with stone walls and a waterfall shower). We encourage you to try the Yahoo Room. It's a western-themed room that has—ye-e-e-e-ehaw!—a wagon-wheeled bed. Rooms cost from $130 to $310 a night. Call (800) 543-9666 or check out the rooms at www.madonnainn.com.

● Washing machine

She'll dig the vibrations when you pop her up onto the Maytag MAV8600 ($770). At 28 inches front-to-back, it gives you both plenty of wiggle room. But the most sex-friendly feature is how the top of the machine is designed. It's not squared off like most other top-loaders. The front edge curves down, which makes it contour perfectly to the back of her bent legs. Almost as if that's exactly what it was meant for. Find a dealer at www.maytag.com.

● National park

If the missus likes to vocalize, pitch your tent in Alaska's Denali National Park, where 6 million untamed acres and a crowd-thinning permit system leave little risk of waking the neighbors. She'll gasp in delight when the midnight sun bathes the Big One (that's Mt. McKinley, buddy) in salmon-pink light. Best: The tundra beneath you is spongy-soft. At least during the summer. Call (907) 683-2294 or visit www.nps.gov/dena.

● Room in your house

We like having sex in the basement—not only because it keeps us close to the Foosball table and the fuse box, but also because of the dark stairwell. Try a doggie-style position with her a few steps above you. Her skin and breasts will brush against the carpeted steps (she'll like that). You'll like the strong upward thrusts you have to make to stay connected.

● Room where you can hide

The walk-in closet. If the door opens in, lean back against it (that'll keep nosy kids from

hot **TIP!**

When researchers asked 40 people to stick their bare hands in freezing water, they found that those who concentrated on sex kept their hands in the water three times longer than those who didn't. Supposedly, sexual fantasies increase tolerance to agony. We know it's true. Our boss has been a pain in the ass all day, and we haven't complained a bit.

prying it open). She climbs on top of you—you can support her weight by holding her under her thighs or under her arms. If your door opens out and the kids do find their naked parents, your alibi is easy and believable. "We're trying on new clothes."

● Room in someone else's house

Our favorite no-getting-caught spot at a friend's party: the garage. Offer to pick up more beer, then slip out the garage door. Nobody will think anything of your being away for 20 minutes, and you can always hide between the two cars if you hear footsteps. Tip: Have her wear a short skirt and no underwear to the party. Quick access makes it easy for you to get in the situation. And easy for you to cover it up if necessary.

● Limousine

The Hummer, of course. More than 25 people can sit in this customized sport-ute. On some models, you can hit a switch so the seats turn into beds. Ultra Coachbuilders in California will build you one of your own—starting at a paltry $65,500. Call (888) 858-7249.

● Hotel chain

The local Come On Inn might save you some cash, but her mood will be much more agreeable if you make reservations at the Four Seasons. She'll like the romantic dining and the deep-soaking two-seater tubs; you'll like the hotel's built-in "quiet zone"—a spot in the hotel that's cornered off from the rest of the guests. You won't hear any kids screaming, and they won't hear you doing the same. Call (800) 819-5053 or visit www.fourseasons.com.

● Stadium

There's plenty of room for extra-inning activity at Olympic Stadium, the home of the Montreal Expos. The team ranked at the bottom in attendance throughout the majors in '99 and 2000, averaging 12,132 fans in a stadium that holds 46,500. Watch out for foul balls . . . and curious television cameramen with zoom lenses.

● Tent

Your best back-to-nature love shack is the Marmot Swallow ($340). You'll love the high ceiling, so you can stand and

Best Car

Our nostalgic choice: A '57 Chevy. For more practical men, it's the Ford Excursion, which measures a romp-friendly 227 inches long. As one salesman put it, "It'll hold 36 sheets of half-inch plywood between the wheel wells." Which is one way of thinking of it.

deliver. Two clear front windows make it a room with a view—you'll be able to spot Ranger Rick coming to investigate the caterwauling. Call (707) 544-4590 or check www.marmot.com for a dealer.

● **Part of a golf course**

Always go for hole 5, 6, 13, or 14. They're the farthest from the clubhouse, which reduces your risk of being caught by gopher-trolling superintendents. The greens are the softest places, but you'll want to use a blanket because courses are usually smothered with pesticides. Try explaining that one to your urologist.

Best Hammock

The King Size Mayan Hammock measures 13 feet long, holds up to 600 pounds of thrashing bodies, and is handwoven from cotton into a diamond-weave pattern that conforms to your shape. And there's enough room for a couple to lie down cross-wise. That reduces your chances of tipping over at the worst possible time. Call (866) 577-3529 or check www.hammocks.com.

● **Waterfall**

After hiking 8 miles into Hawaii's Waimanu Valley, don't linger on the black-sand beach. A wild-pig trail leads up-valley through groves of guava to postcard-perfect Waiilikahi Falls. There, you'll see how the water pulses through a cleft high in the black volcanic rock, cascading through a hundred tiny rainbows into a pool that's so dark and seductive you'll probably need snorkel gear to accomplish what she has in mind.

● **Train**

Charter your own car through Northern Sky Rail Charters of Milwaukee. You'll have your own room, chef, and attendant—and it'll take you anywhere that Amtrak trains go (except the Northeast corridor). Costs vary, but for a romantic getaway, at least it's a little more private than the Times Square shuttle. Call (800) 414-8050 or visit www.northernsky.com.

● **Shower**

Use your own. Just install the Shower for Two showerhead by Europa ($47). It extends 2 feet and rotates in five directions. Turn one stream on your partner to keep her whole body warm and wet, then direct the other on her clitoris. For similar reasons. Call (888) 865-8916.

● **Resort**

The all-inclusive Vatulele Resort in the Fiji Islands has 18 villas, no phones, and romantic dinners served in caves. But that's not why we picked it. Where else

Best Dressing Room

Laura Corn, a California sex expert, told us her trick for doing it in a private spot in a public place: She asks the saleswoman at Victoria's Secret (where they have love seats in many of the dressing rooms) if her date can go into the dressing room to make sure he likes what she's trying on. Corn's experience: The saleswoman always says yes.

can you take day trips to Nooki Nooki Island? Expect to drop a little more than $4,000 for a 4-night (minimum) stay. For reservations, check www.vatulele.com or (800) 828-9146.

● Elevator

"Everybody fantasizes about having sex in an elevator, and the most common place people make that fantasy come true is in hotels," says Patricia Love, author of *Hot Monogamy*. Still, keeping in mind alarms, video cameras, and pubescent tattletale bellhops, we'd prefer you didn't get snagged. Instead, try a freight elevator. It won't have an alarm, and you can stop it between floors for more privacy. One foolproof option for slipping by undetected: Nurse the fantasy until you and your partner are helping a buddy move into a new apartment. Pack the front and sides of the elevator with boxes; leave the middle clear.

● Recliners

After spending a night in a furniture showroom with 50 recliners, our test couple couldn't break away from two in particular. Action-Lane's Comfort King Python ($600) is specifically designed as a "big man's recliner," so it easily supports 350 pounds—100 more than the average chair. The oversize, cushy padding gives you plenty of room to lie back while she straddles you. And hey, it's stain-resistant. See www.action-lane.com. Dutailier's AvantGlide recliner and ottoman ($400 to $500) is actually a glider—it slides front and back, not up and down like a rocker. You can sit on the chair while she rests her hands on the ottoman. With just a little push, the two of you will be in automatic motion. The adventurous couple will enjoy the fact that it swivels 360 degrees. Check www.dutailier.com.

● Cities

If you're retired, enjoy golf, and like eating romantic dinners at 4 in the afternoon, your best bet is Sarasota, Florida, which has 32 percent more single women than men. Younger? We recommend cities where you'll find masses of unattached ladies, which means you should schedule your next trip to New York, Chicago, or Los Angeles.

● Sleeping bag

To get your favorite gymnast in the sack, zip two Sierra Designs Stretch sleeping bags ($139 to $290) together. These synthetic- or down-filled cocoons have elastic ribbing that lets you comfortably bob, squirm, and wrestle into any position. But they still hug your curves so closely that frosty drafts won't sneak in. That's handy when she attempts the double reverse layout with a half twist. Call (800) 635-0461 or visit www.sierradesigns.com.

● Underground spot

At Jewel Cave National Monument in Custer, South Dakota, you can take the half-mile, hourlong walk through a tiny section of the world's third-longest cave system. After a 230-foot elevator ride down to the cave's lighted tunnels, your guide will ask for a volunteer to stay at the back of the group and make sure no one is left behind. Volunteer, then get left behind. Explore her caverns quickly; the guide will periodically check in with you. Click on www.nps.gov/jeca/.

● Mattress

The Simmons Beautyrest Pillow Top ($1,600) has more than 1,000 heavy-duty coils—almost double the number in the average mattress. That makes it appropriate for wild-sex couples—it's firm and durable. Yet it offers a soft, comfortable ride because the top of it is lined with a pillowlike material, part of which is made of cashmere. Trust us, cashmere excites her. Call (800) 628-8738 or check www.mattress.com.

● Playground equipment

Though the merry-go-round has the most potential for dizzying sex, the swings are your best bet for pure sexual satisfaction, without the inner-ear imbalance. Both of you should kneel on the soft ground behind the swing. She leans forward so her elbows fit into the swing seat. Let her gently push the swing forward and back; the movement provides the smooth thrusting. Stay still. And quiet.

● College campus

With a 55-to-45 female-to-male ratio, Florida State University is the most promising prospect of all of *The Princeton Review*'s top-10 party schools. Think of the tans.

● Beach

Hawaii's Kalalau Beach in Na Pali Coast State Park is remote

Best Carpet

We didn't choose the Bigelow Gold Romeo because we feel tragically romantic, but because we hate rug burns. It's well-cushioned and known for its especially smooth, soft surface. Call (800) 227-7381 or check www.carpetone.com.

and often empty (no rangers or lifeguards to cramp your style). The view is incredible in all directions: crystal-blue water in front of you, beautiful green cliffs behind you, a rainbow above you, your smitten hula dancer below you.

● Tourist attraction

This 185-foot tower is a monument to a Canadian general, but with its view of the mist from Niagara Falls and the shore of Lake Ontario, Brock's Monument at Queenston Heights Park in Ontario is also a romantic place for a quickie. The climb to the top is a bit daunting—235 narrow steps up a spiral staircase—but that works to your advantage. Since it's virtually impossible for people to pass one another on the steps, only one group at a time is generally allowed to the top, which gives you several uninterrupted minutes. Get behind her, so you both can look out on the falls. Listen for the gushing. The site is open from May through September.

● Tub

We admire the 6-foot-long Czech & Speake Bath (you can get your very own for $6,600!)—not because it looks like a classic claw-foot tub but because of its design. It's made from two layers of lightweight resin with an air pocket in between. That acts as an insulator to keep your water hot, which means she can linger with Mr. Bubble all night.

● Spring-break spot

Between February and early April, more than 400,000 visitors—and significantly more women than men—descend on Panama City Beach in Florida. Though you probably won't find a quiet spot on the 27 miles of white-sand beaches, you will find a Miss Hawaiian Tropic contest. Treat yourself to a preview at www.springbreakpanamacity.com.

SEX TRENDS

PEEP-TV

The first years of the new millennium saw enough television sex to make Hugh Hefner blush. *Real Sex*, *Temptation Island*, and *Sex and the City*. On *Friends*, Jennifer Aniston made out with Winona Ryder.

Even the news wasn't exempt: When CNN hired Andrea Thompson to be a news anchor, nude photos of her circulated on the Internet.

A study by the Henry J. Kaiser Family Foundation concluded that the number of shows with sexual content rose from 56 percent in the 1997-to-'98 season to 68 percent in the 1999-to-2000 season. And a statistic to make Jerry Falwell cringe: The number of sitcoms with sexual situations rose from 56 percent to 84 percent in 2 years. Sounds good to us.

⦿ Pants

On your ski trip, have her wear the Isis Valkyrie pants and long johns ($290, 802-862-3351, www.isisforwomen.com). They feature the trademarked Split-P system— a strategically placed crotch zipper that unzips fully from front to back. Though it's meant as a convenience for women with small bladders, we endorse other uses. Bonus points if you can figure out how to safely manage a quickie on the lift.

perfect figures

"ME DON'T KNOW YOU GOOD."

First recorded rendering of condoms being used during sex: a painting in a French cave 12,000 to 15,000 years ago

• • • • • • • • •

Fantasy 101

We've discovered an alternate dimension where the rules of relationships don't apply. It's a place where you can have sex with a supermodel without ruining your marriage. Or sample a ménage à trois without causing any jealous feelings. Where is this dimension? It's in your mind. That's right. It's fantasy. Fantasy is more than just the poor-man's pornography—it's a vital part of every guy's sex life. Or at least it should be. Carol Brooks tells you why and how to explore your own secret dimension.

Hard Science

As a kid, you probably were told not to spend time in useless daydreams. But recent research suggests that thinking erotic thoughts can be a major factor in sexual performance as you get older. "Our studies have shown that men have a . . . less developed sexual fantasy life as they get older," says Robert N. Butler, M.D., chairman of geriatrics and adult development at the Mount Sinai School of Medicine in New York City. While the average young man has about seven fantasies a day, the average man in his late 60s has none. Here's what he may be missing.

⦿ Rejuvenated erections

This fading of fantasy comes at a time when, biologically speaking, you need it most. "The number of nocturnal erections a man has starts declining in his 50s," says Irwin Goldstein, M.D., professor of urology at Boston University School of Medicine. Fewer erections means that less nutrient-rich oxygen reaches the tiny muscles of the penis, whose relaxation is key to erection. Fewer nutrients mean more deterioration—and weaker erections. Adding daytime erections, such as the ones that happen during lusty mental imaginings, can help compensate for the nighttime decline.

● Enhanced lovemaking pleasure

Even more compelling is the way in which fantasy can supercharge a man's erections while he is making love to his partner. As you get older, your penis become less sensitive to touch. This makes arousal more dependent on what you're seeing and imagining.

"Roughly 75 percent of men and women have sexual fantasies during sexual activity with their partners," says Harold Leitenberg, Ph.D., professor of psychology at the University of Vermont in Burlington and author of a review of more than 200 studies of fantasies. "Such thoughts are one of the mechanisms we have as humans to naturally enhance arousal. It doesn't mean there's something missing in your relationship or that you find anything about your partner lacking," he adds.

● Sexual innovations

In his book *Sex and Aging*, Dr. Butler emphasizes the importance of continually "reinventing" yourself sexually as a means of staying young and keeping your reproductive equipment in good working condition.

"Fantasy is an excellent way to rehearse an unfamiliar sexual exploit," says Andrew Stanway, M.D., author of *The Joy of Sexual Fantasy*. "Many such exploits are difficult, either because they cause embarrassment or because they present practical problems that must be overcome. Fantasizing gives you the opportunity to explore new sexual acts in your mind before putting your sexual ego on the line."

perfect figures

SO THIS MEANS NO MORE TOPLESS TUESDAYS?

Percentage of companies who say that flirtatious behavior has increased with casual dress codes: 30

The Art of Fantasizing

Although most men know how to fantasize, few develop the talent into an artform—largely because men are never told how or why or given permission to imagine things that they wouldn't necessarily want to do. Here's a short fantasy primer.

● Step 1: Give yourself permission.

A man may be turned on by a fantasy of making love to four women at once, for example, but "if you provided four women for his pleasure, he'd probably run a mile!" says Dr. Stanway. "It's important to keep in mind that most fantasies are not unfulfilled wishes," he says. One way to defeat the guilt trap is to read what other men fantasize about. While erotic videos and stories can provide a great deal of fodder, we found reading the real-life fantasies of dozens of men reported in Bob Berkowitz's *His Secret Life: Male Sexual Fantasies* to be the most freeing. After reading the fantasies of men who prefer group sex, sex with much older and younger women, bondage and spanking, cybersex, and the like, your everyday fantasies may not seem so way out after all.

● Step 2: Relax.

For the ultimate experience, it's critical that you make time and space for yourself in a quiet place where you won't be interrupted. Take several deep breaths.

● Step 3: Heat up.

Dr. Stanway recommends the following imagery for getting yourself in the most erotic state: Imagine that at your feet, some height off the ground, is a large reservoir of a warm, honeylike fluid. Now think of it running via a tube into the soles of your feet. Imagine it coursing up through your body inch by inch. As it approaches your pelvis, imagine it warming up until it's hot. Now feel it fill your scrotum. Feel your testicles enlarging and pulsating with hot honey. "Really concentrate on them filling up and becoming large and heavy," emphasizes Dr. Stanway. Now imagine your penis filling up, becoming thicker, longer, and hotter. Practice until you can develop an erection from this step alone.

hot **TIP!**

Researchers at the New England Research Institute studied 776 men for 9 years and found that those who were sometimes dominant in the bedroom were the least likely to become impotent as they aged. We smell an opportunity to spice up an otherwise routine evening of sex: Let her know who's in charge. "Don't be afraid to initiate sex and guide activities," says William Winkler, Ph.D, a sex therapist in Portland, Oregon. "Don't force your partner, but take the initiative to do what you want to do." Put your partner's hands in your own and direct them to certain areas. Move her body around and position her the way you like. You'll get to do things the way you like them; and she'll probably get a boost from watching you take the lead.

perfect figures

LAUNDRY DAY AGAIN?

Favorite non-bed location where Italian couples report having sex: Washing machines on spin cycle

• • • • • • • • •

● **Step 4: Envision.**

Now is the time to add highly visualized mental pictures. "Men by and large find visually explicit material best," says Dr. Stanway. Take your time composing the scene: Imagine the room or locale in great detail. See the pictures on the wall, the color of the carpet, the plush of the sofa. Smell the faint scent of perfume. Hear the rustle of her clothes as she enters the room.

Foreplay is just as important in fantasy as in reality. Take your time seeing, smelling, feeling every aspect of your fantasy partner. The more richly detailed your mental imaginings, the more explosive the eventual release will be.

THE FUNNY PAGE

"Take it easy—that one's attached to my nipple."

HELP ONLINE

ALL THE NEWS THAT'S UNFIT TO PRINT

Want small talk for your next cocktail party? Stay on top of the news.
The naughty news, that is. Subscribe to Lovenet's World Sex News,
and you'll receive daily "worldwide reports on everything saucy, erotic,
and downright rude." Not only will you be the life of the party, you'll
never forget to participate in National Masturbation Month each May.
Oh, right. You never forget that.
www.world-sex-news.com

NEWS IN THE NUDE

There are no cover-ups on this news team. For $9.95 a month,
you'll get daily news, sports, weather, business, and more
brought to you via e-mail video stream by a nude female
newscaster. Perfect for those of us seeking the naked truth.
www.nakednews.com

GETTING IT ON IN THE GREAT OUTDOORS

Sneaking a roll in the hay just isn't what it used to be, what with
the proliferation of security cameras in barns across America. (Gotta keep
an eye on those mad cows.) If you're ready to move out of the barn
and into the field, check out this excerpt from *Sex in the Outdoors*
by Robert Rose, M.D., and Buck Tilton on a site run by GORP (Great
Outdoor Recreation Pages). It offers tips on how to be discreet
when having sex in the, uh, bush. It also offer tips on how to be nature-
friendly. GORP's advice for minimizing your impact on the environment?
"Make it look as though you never came."
www.gorp.com/gorp/publishers/ics/trv_sexo.htm

MAN'S GUIDE INTERVIEW

Sex through a Window:
A Peep-Show Dancer's Story

An Interview with Julia Query

When word got out that strippers at the Lusty Lady, San Francisco's famed peep palace, wanted to organize into a union, most people laughed. Stripping isn't really work, they said. What could be more fun?

In this interview with Terry Gross on National Public Radio's Fresh Air, Julia Query, a dancer at the club, reveals what it's like on her side of the window. And in her 2000 film Live Nude Girls, Unite!, *which documents the arduous battle she and her fellow peep-show dancers fought for better benefits and more pay, she proves that the job is less about fun than about hard work.*

In fact, we think she makes a compelling argument for the adoption of a national Be Nice to Strippers Week. It doesn't matter what week you choose, just put it on your calendar.

GROSS: [Why did you decide] to dance in a peep show?

QUERY: Well, I had realized that there wasn't much of a career in sociology because there are so few jobs for sociology grad students. And even those that come up are often in places like Kansas, and I didn't want to live in Kansas. So I decided to leave graduate school and follow my first love, which was making art. The problem is that we don't have much funding for artists, so I needed a job that would allow me the time and the flexible schedule to be an artist. And that's the sex industry. I mean, there's a joke in this country: What's the National Endowment for the Arts for women? And the answer is the sex industry. A lot of women in the sex industry are artists.

GROSS: What would you say is the percentage of artists where you work now?

QUERY: I'd guess at least 40 percent of us are working artists right now at the Lusty Lady, and another 40 percent of us are students. And then there's also single mothers.

GROSS: Is this typical?

QUERY: I think it's typical for an urban place. I think in rural places, it's more likely that strippers are single mothers or working mothers with partners. It's good work for the money, and it allows you to be home with your kids during the day if you want to work at night.

GROSS: How good is the money?

QUERY: I get $25 an hour, which is not fabulous; but it's good for a job where I have control over my schedule and can leave for months at a time if I want to tour with a show or work with [my] film and can come back and just pick up where I left off.

> " Cable TV sex channels don't expand our horizons, don't make us better people, and don't come in clearly enough. "
>
> —Bill Maher

GROSS: Let's talk a little bit about what the work is. Describe the room and how people watch and what you're doing in the room.

QUERY: It's an old-fashioned peep show, so guys come into the building, and they'll go into one of 13 little booths that surround a carpeted room with mirrors on the other side of the carpeting. And they'll put in their quarters or their dollars, and the windows will roll up and then they can watch us. There's usually three to five of us in the room, and we're dancing, posing, being seductive. Sometimes we'll drop to our knees and talk to the guy through the window when it's between songs and you can hear him and be a little flirtatious, a little funny. And sometimes it's pretty explicit if you have somebody who only wants to look at one particular body part.

GROSS: How nude are you?

QUERY: I tend to wear heels and some sort of wrap. Some dancers wear nothing except heels. Some dancers wear pretty elaborate costumes, but we're always revealed in certain crucial places.

perfect figures

SURVIVOR 2002: 39 DAYS STRANDED IN A NEVADA BROTHEL

Percentage of Americans who say they would allow a reality-based television show to film them having sex: 8

• • • • • • • • •

GROSS: How did you and the women you work with get the idea of unionizing?

QUERY: Well, for about 8 years prior to my joining the Lusty Lady and starting to work there, [dancers had wanted] to organize around the two-way windows. Two-way windows are windows where the customers could see us but we couldn't see the customers. And through these two-way windows, the customers were videotaping us. They were sneaking in cameras. And we were very worried about these videotapes showing up on the Internet or in porno tapes. And, in fact, it has happened.

So we would complain to management regularly, and management did nothing about it. And they sometimes say things like, "Well, that videotape isn't usual. No camera can really get a very good picture, so you don't have to worry about it," or they'd say, "Oh, well, we're not legally able to stop that because this is legally just an arcade and we can't stop people from using cameras." And we said, "Well, just get rid of the two-way windows," and they said, "No, no, no, we make too much money off of it."

So basically what they said is, "We're making a profit off of having men be able to see you without you seeing them, and we don't care if your health and safety and your well-being are not being respected." It's very hard for dancers to have images taken of them because a lot of us are going into this work prior to getting degrees that are going to let us go out into the world, and we don't want our images out there.

So about 8 months after I was hired, people started getting angry about this again; and I didn't think anything would come of it, because I had heard from so many dancers previously that they had tried to organize and had been unsuccessful. But this time, one dancer, Velvet, went to the Exotic Dancers Alliance meeting, an organization that had started a few years earlier to help dancers organize for better working conditions. They had a contract with Service Employees International Union 790, and they had been told that if dancers wanted to organize for better working conditions that you really had no rights unless you were organizing a union.

And so even though we wanted to sign a petition, we were worried what would happen after we handed it in. And we could have all been fired unless we said we were organizing for a union, and then we were protected by the National Labor Relations Board. Well, we hadn't planned to organize for a union, but we realized that this was the only way to get management to listen to us. And we went ahead and did it, and we had incredible support and unity from the dancers.

GROSS: What are some of the things that you won through unionizing?

QUERY: We won job security. We can no longer be fired for no reason. Any worker in California who isn't covered by a union can be fired at will for no reason at all. So we have a big advantage, by being union workers, over most of the workers in California now. Now they can't fire us unless we've been late a certain number of times or if we aren't doing our job well; whereas before, they generally fired women as soon as they hit the top of the pay scale, because they'd want to hire new women who would work for much less.

We've also won sick days, so we now can call in sick and have somebody else cover our shift. We don't have to find somebody to cover our shift or get points or have our pay cut in half. And we get 2 paid sick days a year.

GROSS: In your movie, you talk about stage fees, which is something relatively new for dancers. Describe what that is.

QUERY: That's when dancers are asked by management to pay them every night that they come to work. In San Francisco, dancers are paying $200 to $400 a night to work. And that means that if it's a slow night, if it's raining out, a woman might not have enough customers who are willing to pay the $40 to $100 for a lap dance. And so when the customer says, "What'll you do for me for $80?" or "Will you give me this? I'll give you a hundred," and she needs to pay management and she needs to pay her babysitter and she needs to pay her rent, she's much more likely to do these illegal acts that she, perhaps, never thought she would be doing—things that make her uncomfortable and can be unsafe. And management is making so much money that they're just hiring more and more and more dancers, so that there's even more competition and dancers are undercutting each other and doing much, much more for much less money.

And the National Labor Relations Board has repeatedly found this practice to be illegal, but they have, to this point, refused to preemptively stop it. Instead they wait for dancers to sue. So if a dancer is willing to never work again, she can sue and get back $10,000, $20,000, $30,000 in stage fees, but she's out of a job.

GROSS: So women who do this kind of dancing could be in the position of owing management money?

QUERY: Mm-hmm. I know a lot of dancers who, if they went through a week or two of having a kind of slump period, would go in every single day owing management money. They had to bring their own money, pay it out, and they could be bankrupt within a week and a half.

GROSS: Since you're [also] a [stand-up] comic who has spent a lot of time working in the sex industry, do you find a lot of the stuff surrounding sex pretty funny?

QUERY: Yes. I think sex is hilarious because it's so uncomfortable-looking. I mean, bodies don't really look like they should fit together like that, do they? And then people's fetishes don't fit their body types. You know, there are tons of men who are kind of older and not fantastic-looking who want to dress like women. And then there are, you know, young men who want to be put in diapers, and they look silly because they're buff and they've got these great big muscles and they look like they're in the military with crew cuts and there they are wearing a diaper and wanting to be told that mommy's going to nurse them.

And so fantasies are so opposite to what they look like. And yet as a sex worker, what you do is you accept them and you love them and you give them what they need, for pay, much like a therapist.

GROSS: Do you think that dancers and other women of the sex industry who actually have direct contact with male customers are putting themselves at risk more than, say, you might be, because the customer might be violent, might be abusive in some way? And there's a lot of women who have private sessions with men, you know, as dancers or . . .

QUERY: Yeah, most of the women I know who do private sessions or who have regulars have no problem at all. Those dancers who have been harmed have been harmed by their boyfriends, just like a third of all women who are killed are killed by their boyfriends or husbands. All men use the sex industry, just about; and in general, they know that what they're doing is they're paying for a fantasy. They kind of forget while they're in the room, and they'll ask questions like, you know, "What do you do for money?" They'll ask me that, and I have to explain, "No, really, I'm a stripper for money." And they'll kind of assume I'm there to have fun, that I'm there to be part of their sexual fantasy because I want to.

GROSS: One more question: Has working with men as your customers in a peep show changed your opinion of men? I mean, you're seeing men in a very unique kind of situation, and it's not necessarily going to bring out the best in them.

QUERY: No, it doesn't bring out the best in them. I've had to accept that everyone has a range in their soul, in their personality. When we're friends with people, they display to us generally their better parts, but they have secrets, too. For instance, I was working on the film with this guy who I liked very much and who I still like, but one day we were out having a drink, and he said something about the first time we met. And I said, "In that class on filmmaking," and he said, "No, at the Lusty Lady" and proceeded to tell me how he knew a client of mine and how he believed we had a really good, wonderful connection. I had spoken to him about sex work. He knew when I was doing one-on-one shows at the Lusty Lady that I always told every customer that he was special, because that's my job, and that, of course, I didn't remember him from this experience. And it made me kind of nauseous there, having this drink with him, to think that he thought of me that way or thought that it had been a real experience.

> **"** It's hard to sit in your boxers and jerk off in front of people for 3 hours. **"**
>
> —Philip Seymour Hoffman, on making the 1998 film *Happiness*

But later, I was able to accept that he paid to have a sexual fantasy. It's nice that he still is getting use out of the 20, 40 bucks that he paid for that sexual fantasy. It's kind of my job as a sex worker to not bust his fantasy, to let him have his fantasy because he's paying for it. He's got a girlfriend. He doesn't cheat on her. He's a good person.

And that's okay.

QUICKIES

OH GOD! OH GOD!

During the European broadcast of a mass from the Vatican, the audio feed got switched with that of a pornographic channel, Salon.com reports. We're not sure who deserves more pity: mass watchers forced to endure loud moans and bass-slapping soul music, or the Fantasy Channel watchers forced to listen to prayers in Latin.

I KNOW HOW YOU FEEL, MR. PRESIDENT

In the end, it wasn't the fact that the Reverend Jesse Jackson admitted to fathering a love child that was so dumbfounding. Nor was the fact that his mistress was an official at Jackson's Rainbow/PUSH Coalition, which reportedly paid the woman $35,000 in "moving expenses" and "consulting services."

What was truly astonishing was that while the married, father-of-five Jackson was carrying on his affair, he was counseling Bill Clinton about his transgressions with Monica Lewinsky. This made humor headlines when Jay Leno quipped that it was probably Jackson who gave the prez that infamous cigar.

SEX LOSES ITS GRAND MASTER

Sex pioneer William Masters died in February 2001 of complications from Parkinson's disease. He was 85.

Masters, a gynecologist, and his psychologist wife, Virginia Johnson, got together in the late 1950s and spent the next 10 years wiring up copulating couples in the lab and recording every shake, rattle, and roll. The result was the book *Human Sexual Response*, in which they identified four phases in the sexual response cycle: excitement, plateau, orgasm, and resolution. Over the next 25 years, other important books followed: *Human Sexual Inadequacy* and *Human Sexuality*.

Some of the couple's findings were criticized and debunked, but their work helped foster candid discussions about sex. Masters once said, "When things don't work well in the bedroom, they don't work well in the living room, either." Smart man.

THE POLITICS OF DIVORCE

Making your wife a political adversary is never a good idea. Not if you want spend a quiet evening at home . . . with your girlfriend.

The divorce between New York City mayor Rudolph W. Giuliani and estranged wife Donna Hanover is a perfect example of why it's better to have a private life that's, well, private. Still living together in the same house, the couple has been entertaining the public with revolving injunctions and court battles since the fall of 2000. They've been downright malicious toward each other. He stopped her from getting Yankees tickets; she banned his girlfriend from Gracie Mansion. He stripped her of her staff and public duties; she sued for the cost of a press secretary.

Makes arguing over the CD collection seem kinda wimpy.

CELL-PHONE FUN

Hate cell phones? Here's something that'll change the way you think about them: A study conducted in Australia by Virgin Mobile showed that one in 15 Aussies has engaged in cell-phone sex (yes, people actually study these things). So we talked to sex expert Anne Semans, author of *The New Good Vibrations Guide to Sex*, to see how Americans can get in on this trend from Down Under. Her suggestions:

● Take your phone to the middle of a crowded public park, then call your partner at home and make her squirm. This is probably the closest you'll ever get to pleasing her in such a public place—unless your weekly budget covers bail money.

● When you're stuck in traffic, call each other and talk dirty. Bring people from cars around you into your fantasies (by describing them, not tapping on their windows). Suddenly, you're having group sex on a crowded freeway.

> **"** I'm too shy to express my sexual needs except over the phone to people I don't know. **"**
>
> —Garry Shandling

● Use your cell phone in conjunction with her remote-control vibrating panties. Then go to a crowded bar and sit far enough apart so that you can see each other but not hear each other. Call her on your phone and talk dirty while you remotely give her a buzz.

ASK THE SEX DOC

Q: *Is watching scrambled porn bad for my TV, or even worse, for me?*
—J. T., Weston, Massachusetts

A: Your TV doesn't care whether the girl you're gawking at is scrambled or not. It just receives and displays the signal it gets. If the TV projects an image that's unwatchable, it doesn't strain to do it. As for the physical effect it may be having on you, even people who are prone to photosensitive epilepsy are generally safe watching scrambled television, says Mark S. Yerby, M.D., of Portland, Oregon, an expert on seizure disorders. But do yourself a favor: Pay the cable bill.

Q: *My partner and I enjoy a daring sex life. How reliable are condoms under wet conditions, such as in a sauna, underwater, and so on?*
—T. W., Arlington, Virginia

A: Your main problem is the risk of the condom slipping off. Bath oils, bubble baths, and chlorine can weaken the rubber, so if you're after splashy sex, head for the sea.

Short bursts of heat won't be a problem, so quickies in the sauna are okay. But boiled rubbers—such as those kept in a car glove compartment—are accidents waiting to happen since condoms cook in intense, prolonged heat.

Snowbound hanky panky, on the other hand, is just fine—after all, condoms can be stored safely in the fridge. But while you're there, don't be tempted to introduce ice cream into your lovemaking: It's another thing that will damage the rubber. And if you've ever fantasized about having a quickie on the x-ray conveyor belt at the airport, you'll be relieved to hear that x-rays are condom-friendly.

The Sex Doc is a fictional character.
The actual advice was provided by a variety of
medical doctors and other qualified experts.

SIDESTEP
THE SEX POLICE

Like everything else fun in life, sex has rules. Break them and you're screwed.

Tell a co-worker she looks nice—face a lawsuit. Read a racy office e-mail—time to update your résumé. Keep secrets from your wife—meet her in divorce court. Get caught having sex in your future mother-in-law's house—dodge her wrath till death do you part.

Even fantasy comes with a price: Indulge one and worry about winding up dead instead of in bed.

While we don't mean this section to scare you, we want to help you avoid the penalties of sexual slipups. Keep reading, and you won't get burned when things get hot.

TOP TEN

Ways to Have Stealth Sex

Somehow, sex without moans, squeals, and the occasional howl doesn't seem complete. But sometimes, you and your mate have to hit the mute button because of get-a-life neighbors or visiting in-laws who shouldn't be subjected to the sounds of you defiling their virtuous daughter. Guess what? Sneaky can be fun. Here's how to stay under the radar when you're under the covers.

1 **Seal cracks.** Weather-strip the inside of your bedroom door frame and put a threshold seal (find one at a hardware store) along the bottom of the door. If you can see light through the cracks, sound will go through, too.

2 **Buy a scrap piece of carpet . . .** and place it up against your door. Heavy carpets and wall hangings are good for absorbing noise, says Bennett Brooks, president of Brooks Acoustic Corporation. The more fuzzy stuff you have in your room, the quieter it'll be.

3 **Go under cover.** Down pillows and blankets are heavier than most other materials, so they usually muffle sound more effectively.

4 **Turn on the shower.** The in-laws will hear water running through the pipes of the house and won't hear you.

5 **Raid her closet.** Try a stand-up quickie in her closet. It's likely to be jam-packed from floor to ceiling with sound-dampening dresses and skirts and such. Plus, the closet door will subdue your sounds.

6 **Hit the deck.** If your squeaky bed is the problem, move to the floor (or a chair). Lying atop a soft blanket will further stifle your squeals—not to mention protect against rug burn.

7 **Play Barry White.** Strong bass sounds disguise low-frequency noises—like the headboard thumping against the wall, Brooks says. To conceal squeaking, you're better off with music that also squeaks. Think Britney.

8 **Silence your Sealy.** To do away with mattress squeak permanently, ditch the bed frame and put your box spring and mattress on the floor. If that seems too drastic a measure, at least place your bed against a wall not shared with another bedroom.

9 **Create some noise.** White noise, that is. In the guest room. Run a fan, air conditioner, or sound box that plays soothing sounds like ocean waves. It's sure to drown out the clamor coming from your room.

10 **Gag each other.** Add some kink to your lovemaking and quiet things down at the same time with this S&M trick. For those inexperienced in bondage play, we suggest starting off with soft restraints such as a silk scarf or panty hose. Who knows? Maybe the whips and chains will be next. Of course, that could get noisy. . . .

MUST READS

Love Advice from Lawyers

These days, the deck is pretty well stacked against happily ever after. If you want any shot at being together when the credits roll, you need the kind of advice most guys don't get until lawyers become involved—and then it costs $200 an hour. Here, Andrew Taber has a few tips from the professionals we hope you never need.

I'm getting married this summer. She's perfect, I've ordered the tuxes, and the honeymoon is booked, but I'm still scared. Not about making a lifelong commitment or whether she's the right one—it's the odds that make me nervous. Two million two hundred fifty-six thousand couples will wed this year, but another 1,135,000 will file for divorce.

To avoid seeing the dark side of the aisle, I talked to everyone from clergy to psychologists—I even listened to that Mars-Venus book on tape. Ironically, the best advice I heard about staying together came from the people who'd benefit most if my new wife and I split apart.

Divorce lawyers. They see the twisted wreckage of bad marriages on a daily basis, so they know better than anyone what makes good love go bad. "Just follow these 10 rules," they told me, "and you'll never see any of us again."

❶ Let her nag.

If she's bugging you to pick up your clothes or reshingle the roof, congratulations: She's helplessly, hopelessly in love. "I've never seen a marriage end because a woman nagged too much, but I've seen the opposite," says Brook Radelfinger, a family lawyer in San Francisco. Her years of interviewing unhappy couples have convinced her that a hassling spouse is one who's still vigorously engaged in the marriage. "When the nagging stops, it's a sign that one partner has thrown in the towel," she says.

❷ Share the wealth.

Couples are marrying at older ages, which means each partner goes to the altar with a lucrative 401(k), a bulging stock portfolio, and rigid financial values. To protect their money, a lot of these couples choose to keep their finances separate.

Be wary—that strategy may not pay dividends over time. When you don't share, it tells your spouse that your Twentieth Century Ultra is more important to you than she is. "Having separate accounts is one common denominator in the marriages I've seen fail," says Glen L. Rabenn, a family-law specialist in southern California. Our suggestion: Never marry a woman you wouldn't trust to sign your checks.

❸ Live within your means.

Our lawyers put it simply: The more money you owe, the more likely you are to divorce. "More than half of the people who come to me are divorcing because of money issues," says Radelfinger. So even if Bruiser and Rocco aren't looking to repossess your kneecaps, unpaid bills and maxed-out credit cards can lead you to consider exit strategies—not only from the crushing debt but also from the union that produced it.

Before you marry, work out how much money you and your wife will invest, put into savings, and use for trips and vacations. And be honest—better she finds out now that you're a tightwad.

❹ Plan your kids' religion.

You're Buddhist, she's a Druid. When it's just the two of you, an interfaith relationship can be chic; it's a sign that you're open and enlightened. But when you have to decide how to raise the kids, suddenly your wife thinks you're Satan because you won't worship the Japanese maple.

Your goal: Avoid eternal damnation—and divorce—by agreeing on the kids' religious upbringing before they're even born. "When divorce happens because of religion, it's almost always because of the kids," says Radelfinger.

❺ Spend time, not money.

Money can buy a lot of things: houses, vacations, the silence of witnesses. What it can't buy is a happy marriage. "I had a client who gave his wife jewelry, cars, trips, and furniture," says Valerie J. Botter, a domestic-relations attorney in Massachusetts. "He was shocked when, after 26 years, she left him. He figured

SEX TRENDS

WHAT'S IN A NAME?

Like to sneak porn peeks at work? It's tempting on one of those don't-feel-like-doing-anything-constructive Fridays. We sex-book publishers get away with it because, well, it's written into our job descriptions. But when it isn't? Take a lesson from former University of Minnesota professor Richard Pervo. Last February, Pervo (yep, that's his real name, we double-checked) was found with nearly 4,000 images of child pornography on his university computer. After police seized two-dozen computer disks, more than 100 CDs, and printed pictures of naked girls, Pervo lost his tenured position as professor of religious studies and Christianity. And he lost his good name.

he'd bought her loyalty, but she wanted more than just things; she wanted companionship. She was lonely."

Instead of playing the big spender, put some thought into gifts that show her you know and support her interests—a first-edition book by her favorite

Just in Case . . .

If divorce is the only answer, here are five strategies to ensure that she doesn't stick it to you.

1 Hire the best lawyer you can afford. "In the game of divorce, the strength of your lawyer makes all the difference," says Dominic Barbara, a New York divorce attorney who hosts cable TV's *Power of Attorney*. If your lawyer is a ball buster, he says, hers will be more open to settling. To find a force to be reckoned with, grill the clerks at your local divorce court. They know which lawyers are consistent winners.

2 Throw her a bone. Giving your wife something she wants up front—the nicer car, the dachshund, a few extra bucks—before going to court can defuse her anger and show her you're willing to work things out, says Glen L. Rabenn, a family-law specialist in southern California. Giving in on small things early can lead to bigger wins down the road.

3 Do your homework. Busy men forget a lot of things—"like the birthdays of their own kids," says renowned New York City divorce attorney and media personality Raoul Felder. Fumbling family facts doesn't make you a bad father, but the judge won't know that. If you want custody, remind yourself of the key statistics— such as age, grade, den mother, friends, and whether they like chunky or smooth peanut butter— in case the judge asks. Don't leave any doubt in the judge's mind that you're a caring, competent parent, says Felder.

4 Don't lose your temper. Some lawyers tell their clients to taunt their husbands—even slap or poke them—to provoke them into lashing back. One Polaroid of a reddened wrist and your chances of a fair divorce are over. "Baiting poet, tickets to see the hockey team she's loved since childhood. And stop saying no to those ballroom-dancing classes.

6 Take baby steps.
A lot of Radelfinger's cases involve new parents. The most common variation on the theme: Couple has problems, couple decides baby will fix problems, baby comes, problems grow worse, divorce and really big child-support payments follow.

The solution? Anticipate that there will be rough spots. Every marriage is hard at the same predictable times—when one of the partners is changing careers, for example, or when the pair is having a baby or sending a kid to college. When a man and woman hit a pothole they didn't see coming, they think something is wrong with their marriage. They panic, and that's when they make the decision to divorce.

7 Get your touch back.
Married men tend to touch their wives only when they're looking for sex. Lawyers say that's a mistake. "Men underestimate the power of nonsexual touch," Radelfinger says. Women who come to her looking for a divorce often talk about how their husbands no longer hold their hands or offer unsolicited kisses and back rubs—all the things that make women feel emotionally connected. "Most of the marriages I see could have been helped—if not saved—if the husbands had learned to be more affectionate," she says.

8 Keep her in the loop.
Spending more time with your secretary than with your wife? Even if you're not fooling around,

or claiming abuse where there wasn't any is a quick—and common—way to get someone kicked out of the house," says San Francisco family lawyer Brook Radelfinger. Once you're out, her claim for primary custody, and the house, gains strength.

5 Live like a monk until the papers are signed. During the trial, her lawyer may tap your phone, have you followed, and interrogate your friends and colleagues looking for dirt. If he can prove you're a sleaze, it makes his job easier, says Felder. Don't give him the ammunition. If you think you're being followed, fine, let them follow you—to Bible study, volunteer night at the homeless shelter, and your kids' basketball games.

your marriage could be headed for trouble. "If you're married to your job and not available to your partner, you're being unfaithful in a way," Botter says. Many of her cases unfurl like this: A husband becomes a workaholic and emotionally absent. His wife, starving for a connection, has a brief affair. He can't get over the tryst and files for divorce, while all she wanted in the first place was to get him back.

To keep her happy—and still keep your job—share your day with her and ask about hers. Tell her about the fight you had with your boss, the deal you closed, the giraffe you made out of pencil stubs. It's a simple way to keep the relationship current and connected, says Lynne Gold-Bikin, former chairwoman of the American Bar Association's family-law section.

9 Don't be afraid to argue.
Lawyers see a lot of couples who don't fight—except in court. The reason? Their marriages are so passionless they can't even muster a good argument.

So air your dirty laundry, but learn to fight fair. Ask for change instead of demanding it, suggests Gold-Bikin. "Use 'I' sentences—I notice, I feel, I want—to eliminate the accusatory tone," she says.

And never blurt out the word *divorce*. It changes the dynamic of the relationship by taking away the underlying premise that you'll make up. Now all future disagreements have the possibility of a split lurking in the background. "Just mentioning divorce in a disagreement raises the level of conflict," Botter says.

10 Make smart moves.
Many of the clients that divorce lawyers see are new to town. The reason: Long-distance moves often presage divorce. Usually one partner is starting a new job—providing instant access to new friends and social activities—while the other is tagging along discontentedly in his or her wake. "I just had a case in which the woman

hot **TIP!**

In a moment of indiscretion, a man picks up a girl and finds himself straddled in a cab on the way to her place. But he's sitting on his cell phone, and his unusually adroit buttocks press the first number in memory: his girlfriend's. She answers to hear his muffled voice, some girl giggling, and Ravi Shankar music playing in the background. He doesn't realize until he gets home that she has heard it all. If you're ever caught in a similar situation (and we certainly hope you are), just turn off the phone. If you are expecting an important call and must leave it on, learn the code you need to dial (look in the owner's manual) to block outgoing calls.

was so unhappy she didn't even discuss it with her husband," says Rabenn. "She just packed her bags, took the kids, and moved back."

If you're on the move, take this tip from Radelfinger: Budget in the cost of flying in a few friends and family for regular visits. Even if you can't stand your mother-in-law, having her come for a month or two may be worth it. "Maintaining that connection with familiar people, especially while you're getting settled, will help your wife make the transition," she says.

perfect figures

THAT MAKES IT EVEN MORE FUN.

Number of states in which
oral sex between a
married man
and woman is illegal:
9

SWF, Armed and Dangerous

In the movies, nothing is sexier than a chick who kicks ass. In real life, the ones with guns aren't always the best prospects. Shane DuBow discovered this firsthand, and wrote about it for GQ.

It's weird. Sometimes you need a little sanity—a quiet return to routine—and sometimes you need just the opposite, something to jolt you out of your zone of comfort (or misery) and, in theory, help you remember what's good and special about eating food, breathing air, walking barefoot in the new morning grass with the whippoorwills whippoorwilling and what all, that kind of thing. That the second part, the path to renewed vigor, often demands engaging in the sort of risk that later makes you appear either plucky or stupid, depending on your results, is the hazard of adventure. And in matters of the heart, it's the thrill of, for example, agreeing to date a woman unlike any woman you've dated before. A woman of extremes. A woman of unpredictability. A woman whose advertisements, in my case, in this one instance had me scrambling toward my door (upon hearing her knock) with the barely repressible urge to fling it open and embrace her or, alternatively, pat her down.

I'd been promised by my buddy Phil, see, that she, my blind-date-to-be, would look like Kate Moss. I'd been reminded, by Phil again, that I was a still-wounded romantic doofus (I'd just been dumped) and that Kate Moss was, you know, pretty much a famous supermodel. And then there was Phil's wife, who'd added, "Not just Kate Moss, you doofus, but Kate Moss with breasts."

Still, it wasn't until I'd made one last skeptic's call to one last mutual friend that I'd learned the lone detail that would make this blind date, my first ever, seem like a must-do, must-try, one-time chance to flirt with amorous danger and perhaps feel reenergized. The detail being that in addition to everything else, this improbably single superbabe who improbably wished to meet me also happened to carry a gun.

"But seriously," I said.

"Seriously," the friend said. "She keeps it on her—she says it's her constitutional right."

Visions of a Second Amendment tigress crept through my head. I pictured a Bond babe with militia-style shoes. I saw an Amazon warrior of decisive action and self-assured calm, a woman of mystery whose ballistic baggage called to mind a titillating capacity for strong feelings and wild nights, not to mention an impulsive disregard for consequences, which might, I thought, lead to guilt-free sex. Either that or it might lead, in the event of some random street crime, to my companion's laying down some suppressing fire while I made for the car.

And then, before I felt ready, she was inside. Inside and pecking my cheek. Inside and beaming out a wry, white-toothed wattage as if our smoochy greeting, this setup, her very presence in my apartment, were some kind of shared joke. Her height, thank God, was not supermodel height. Her face was dazzlingly pretty, though, and her hair did possess a shampoo-commercial bounce, and I did find it hugely impossible not to scan the rest of her personage for suspicious bulges or other telling signs.

A Secretly Holstered Confidence

For starters, she sighed something about her long workday and thanked me for accommodating her eleventh-hour change of plans—from drinks on the town (too exhausting) to dinner at my place (was I cool with that?). Meanwhile, her shoulder bag stayed on her shoulder, slung toward her hip, bulging a bit beyond what you'd expect from, say, a cell phone and a spare lipstick.

I poured us each a jelly-jar glass of wine. I managed to survive a few minutes of blather wherein I strove to (a) hide my emasculating antigun bias and (b) hide my goofy urge to discover exactly which of Charlie's Angels she dug most. (I'd always been a Sabrina fan myself, and wouldn't it be great if she were, too?) Beyond that, I didn't have much of a plan, other than this: Before I ran out of smart things to say, I'd turn to my cooking so as to transfer the bulk of our conversation's weight onto the one person, between the two of us, who might kill for food.

Her name, I knew, was Beth. She was 27 to my 29. She'd gone to a good college. Enjoyed football. Liked her parents, one of whom—her mother, I'd been told—had once penned an NRA-friendly personal essay about arms-bearing empowerment. For her job, I gathered, Beth did some kind of corporate marketing. As she breezed over the ups and downs of her past few years, I detected coy references to rich boyfriends and ex-otic trips, and her eyes, blue-green and wide, appeared supercharged by an enviable confidence that, I just knew, had a secretly holstered source.

All I wanted to know about, I realized, was the gun. *What about the gun, I wanted to scream, the gat, the heat, your piece? Like, what's up with that? Where do you keep it, why do you keep it, what kind is it, have you ever used it, and how much ammo do you think we'll need to get us through dessert?* But because I wanted neither to confront her—she might take offense—nor own up to my cowardly research, I scoped in on her shoulder bag and sublimated my curiosity into suggestive terms: "Well, shoot, a girl like you sets her sights on something, I bet you hit what you aim at, right? I mean the caliber of girl you are . . ." etcetera.

In response, Beth batted her eyes, refilled her jelly jar and invited me to explain why a nice boy like me didn't at this very moment have a full-time girlfriend. I puffed my cheeks to stall. The good thing was that, so far, I hadn't overboiled dinner. The bad thing was that Beth's question felt like a real stumper—if you're so great, why are you so single?—not to mention a too-quick trespass into my private emotional space, the

---

hot TIP!

Fellow gets the hots for his girlfriend's best friend and starts seeing her on the side. One night, he forgets that his old flame has caller ID. He calls from her best friend's place to cancel a date, and they're both instantly busted. Don't want that to happen to you? On most phone systems, you can keep your number from being displayed by dialing a special code beforehand. In our area, it's *67, and the service is free. This results in "private" or "unknown" appearing on the phone of whomever you're calling. Of course, you risk their mistaking you for a replacement-window salesman and not picking up, but in this guy's case, that would have saved him. Check with your phone-service provider to see what you have to do to make it work in your area.

kind of trespass you normally don't allow, if you've got any rocks, until after you've at least run through a few hours' chitchat re: your favorite bands, your zaniest wedding-party antics or, if you're drinking with purpose, the wondrously warm bite of your favorite new hooch.

But then, I wondered, wasn't such a spontaneous trespass the very sort of anything-goes attitude I'd wanted to rub up against? Plus, there was still the matter of Beth's shoulder bag and its (almost certainly) loaded contents and the way said contents seemed to compel a response. So . . . so . . . the reason for my singleness, I stammered, had to do with my stomped-on heart and my fear of new scars and the way those details, when confessed up front, tended to make the few women I'd recently met lose my phone number or, in at least one case, move to Frisco.

"Well," Beth said abruptly, settling her eyes on me in a way that seemed unflinchingly lewd, "you don't have to worry about that with me, okay, because I'm not looking for anything."

At this point, I should mention, our date was only 30 minutes old. And yet already I felt encouraged. Maybe it was the wine. Or Beth's swaggering vibe. Or the way being in Beth's gun-toting company kept me feeling so refreshingly on edge. Or maybe it was just that here we were, kinda hitting it off in my little breakfast nook, recklessly defying all the meet-for-a-drink public-safety rules made to afford either blind-date party a yawning "big day tomorrow" ease of escape.

We ate in the living room on the floor, with flickering candles and a D'Angelo CD, because D'Angelo, I thought, seemed like the sort of sexually frank nerve-soothing crooner you'd want to play for a girl who wasn't looking for anything but had invited herself (and her bulging shoulder bag) over, sight unseen.

So there we were, just me, Beth, and Beth's bag, which she'd set down beside her, well within quick-draw reach. I'd made spaghetti with clams—lots of aphrodisiacal little quahogs—

SEX TRENDS

WHERE DO WE SIGN UP?

University of Washington researchers found that 21 percent of 165 college men reported being the object of unwanted sexual attention. Women were even hanging around parties and waiting for guys to get drunk. "They then hit on them when the men were unable to make rational decisions about sex," says study author Mary E. Larimer, Ph.D. Slow down, doc, you lost us on the "rational decisions" bit.

and Beth, unlike most of the other attractive women I'd known, showed no signs of self-consciousness about stuffing her face. Great, I thought. Everything's great. Beth likes to eat. Beth likes to drink. Beth likes to throw herself into things and . . . look exasperated as she pitches her fork down onto her plate?

What, I wondered, was the problem?

The answer, according to Beth, only halfway through her second serving, was that I hadn't yet kissed her, and now she wanted to know why that might be. I forced an uncertain grin. Aside from the fact that I'd just met her and we were still eating, what could I say? The effect of her question, however, was to make me unsure about my position. Was this rush to smooch some blind-date protocol I knew nothing about, the sort of thing I should have expected based on Beth's cut-to-the-chase attitude about everything else? Or was something bigger going on, something to do with age-old gender dynamics being inverted by Beth's hidden artillery? Was she being emboldened? Was I being enfeebled? Or non sequiturally, was this the time to confess my lingering ambivalence about finding someone new or figuring out what to look for when the caring, intelligent qualities I'd previously wanted had most recently led to a relationship that lacked surprises, a relationship I figured a blind date with La Femme Nikita here would help me blast past?

A Known Loose Cannon

What I did then, in lieu of bluff, disclosure, or stall, was take inspiration from her bravado and get busy with my lips. Got into some industrial-strength lip action with much tongue and perhaps too much heavy breathing on Beth's part, though for my money the lip action was plenty engrossing, and at any rate, I was willing to be deceived. At least until Beth pulled back, maybe 3 minutes into our groping, and began to cry.

Scenes from *Fatal Attraction* looped through my head. I saw my joint-custody dog boiled in a pot. I saw tabloid headlines like DOOFUS GETS HIS DUE. I saw TV pundits asking rhetorically about what the young doofus might have been thinking, entertaining a known loose cannon at his place on blind-date number one?

I rested a hand, at arm's length, on the loose cannon's warm back. I tried to adopt an air of ready-to-help support. I twisted about to locate the exact proximity of her bag. And I tried not to take cover when, moments later, she reached her right hand into that bag in search of—it turned out—a pale-blue tissue.

It's not that I actually, literally feared getting shot. But given the unpredictable unraveling of Beth's psyche, I felt a tad leery of what might come next. I said, "What, um, what's wrong, Beth? Did I do something wrong, because, I mean, I didn't mean to do something wrong or make you cry or anything bad like that, because, you know, I just met you and I already like you and, no, seriously, I like you and . . ."

Beth was shaking her head. Beth was hooking a stray piece of hair behind her left ear. Beth was snorting into her tissue and collecting her wind. "Don't you think it's sad," Beth said, "that everyone else can fall in love and people like us just can't?"

People like us.

I blinked slowly and tried to breathe. A part of me wanted to smash dishes and scream out against my unbelievably rotten luck, the I-should-have-known-better unfairness of the night's psychotic turn. And another part of me still wanted to root around in Beth's bag and touch the cold steel corporality of her gun. Stray, unutterable thoughts kept zinging through my head. Thoughts like, "Help please, oh God, someone please help." Or like, "Hey, for your information, Beth, lost love is what left me willing to seek your company in the first place, Ms. People-Like-Us, the thing you and your presumed gun-slinging independence were supposed to help me forget." Like, "I wanted to feel empowered by our association, you know? Wanted to think of myself as a rowdy, bring-it-on kind of dude. Wanted you to be the kind of noncloying free-spirited dudette who proved both racy (in the manner of the heavily armed) and safe (in the manner of one who wouldn't need me more than I needed her)."

> " The difference between pornography and erotica is lighting. "
>
> —Gloria Leonard

Our evening sputtered forth. I kept my movements slow. Beth made one worrisome, bag-in-hand trip to the john—my chance to bolt?—only to emerge apologetic and endearingly sheepish. And then our date, for lack of better options, resumed with more kissing, as Beth didn't seem inclined to head home and I couldn't very well leave my own apartment, and at least if I kept her kissing, I kept myself safe. Okay, I also kept myself in the hunt for some between-the-sheets expeditioning, a difficult urge to snuff out, even when the pursuit of that urge meant prolonging my already awkward association with the possibly insane.

The result? A stumbling, inexorable progression toward my futon, followed by my performance, at Beth's urging, of a sexual act that typically involves some implicit quid pro quo but that in this case did not. Reason enough, I thought as Beth redressed and I reevaluated my read on her for the umpteenth time, to make a case for stricter gun control, as there are people in this world who obviously can't be trusted to honor our most basic social contracts. Reason enough, too, I decided (as Beth bid me a suddenly shy, I'm-really-not-that-sort-of-girl adieu), to rethink my reasons for having her over in the first place.

It wasn't merely that I'd been bored or lonely or carnally out of practice. It was that I'd longed for a certain sense of far-flung possibility, a certain sense that a home-based blind date with a gun-slinging superbabe promised to unleash. Now, though, with Beth (and her shoulder bag) just departing and a post-roller-coaster daze filling my eyes, I felt at once sad for her (all that bluster, all that fear) and disappointed with myself. Disappointed that I'd never found a suave way to confirm or refute the existence of her high-powered hardware (though, in retrospect, the idea of it was what mattered most) and disappointed, too, for supposing that a girl with a gun might by virtue of her armaments give me a quick new path to salvation, a reason to wake up.

You've Got Mail: And Oh, by the Way, You're Fired

The button marked "forward" at the top of your in-box might as well read "fire me." You may think those jokes about Raquel Welch in the lifeboat—the ones your cousin keeps sending—are too funny to keep to yourself. Twenty-nine of your closest co-workers might even agree. That one person who doesn't? She holds your entire career in her hands. Forward that e-mail when you shouldn't, and people won't just laugh. They'll make sure you're escorted from the building by armed guards. Before you click, read this warning from Joshua Green that originally appeared in Playboy.

You've seen them. Hell, you've even passed them along to buddies and co-workers: humorous e-mail with titles such as "25 Reasons Why Beer Is Better Than Women."

Beer doesn't demand equality.

A frigid beer is a good beer.

For the opposite sex, there are "10 Reasons Why Cucumbers Are Better Than Men," followed by "Why Beer Is Better Than Cucumbers." Electronic mail has taken the place of the watercooler. Heard a good one lately? Pass it around. Or add your own. Relieve some stress. Share a chuckle.

Some people, however, aren't laughing. In 1995, four women who worked for Chevron received messages they considered offensive, including the infamous odes to beer mentioned previously. They printed out the e-mail, hired lawyers, and slapped the company with a sexual-harassment suit. The women said the e-mail contributed to a hostile environment. Rather than go to trial, Chevron agreed to pay the women $2.2 million as well as court and legal fees.

That same year, a woman who worked for Microsoft sued the company for sexual discrimination, claiming she had not been promoted because of her gender. She argued that the company had created an environment hostile toward women. Among her evidence: e-mail distributed by colleagues on topics such as "mouse balls," a proposed sex holiday in Finland, and a parody titled "A Girl's Guide to Condoms." A judge sided with the woman, ruling that the messages could be used as evidence to argue that Microsoft does discriminate.

In 1996, the Principal Financial Group insurance company dismissed a customer service representative because she had forwarded to colleagues e-mail messages with titles such as "A Few Good Reasons Cookie Dough Is Better Than Men" and "10 Reasons Why Trick-or-Treating Is Better Than Sex." The woman took the company to court, arguing that she had been dismissed unfairly. Her employer responded that she had violated e-mail and sexual-harassment policies, and that it had the evidence in hand. A judge ruled that the company had not proved that employees who received the e-mail felt harassed. He also ruled that the company had not adequately warned the woman that sending personal e-mail on her work computer could get her fired. However, Principal was not ordered to rehire the woman, nor to pay her. The bottom line: She lost her job.

Surveillance Protects the Bottom Line

One survey of visitors to an online careers site found that 90 percent of those with access to computers at work had visited at least one Web site last year that couldn't be justified as helping them do their jobs (the other 10 percent are lying, or they're the sort of culturally numb automatons George Orwell envisioned). According to the same survey, 84 percent of American workers with computers have sent or received personal e-mail on the job. A report last year by an Internet filtering firm estimated that about one-third of the time an employee spends online at work is for recreation. The survey did not indicate how much "recreational" time these employees spent chatting with workers before the age of computers or how many have made personal phone calls related to raising a family or conducting the business of life.

Many companies fear the Internet. It creates costly lawsuits. So they have turned to surveillance to protect the bottom line. Forty-five percent of the companies that responded to an American Management Association survey admitted that they monitor phone calls, check computer files, and read incoming and outgoing e-mail messages. A survey of 200 human resources managers found that 1 in 3 had fired someone for misuse of on-line resources. In all, an estimated 40 million Americans are working under some type of surveillance.

In November of 1999, the New York Times Company fired 23 workers from its central processing center in Norfolk, Virginia, for distributing pornographic images and jokes via e-mail. An anonymous tipster prompted the bloodletting. That same month, the Navy disciplined more than 500 people at a supply depot in Pennsylvania for exchanging racy cartoons, photos, and jokes. In October of the same year, Xerox fired 40 people for visiting online casinos, sex sites, eBay, and E-trade. But those who kept their jobs aren't necessarily breathing a sign of relief. The company routinely monitors the Web use of each of its 92,000 employees.

In the years since Anita Hill accused Clarence Thomas of boorish behavior, the courts have rewritten laws that govern the workplace, to clamp down on any discussion of sex that could be construed as harassment. That discussion now includes both e-mail messages and Web sites.

The laws against sex discrimination originally sought to prohibit the quid pro quo demand that a person sleep with his or her boss, or lose the job. But the government also targeted something it called a "hostile sexual environment"—workplace behavior that is sexual in nature and judged to be unreasonable, pervasive, and unwelcome to at least one person.

perfect figures

"SORRY, DEAR, I JUST CAN'T EAT YOUR KANGAROO SURPRISE ANYMORE."

Percentage of unfaithful husbands in Australia who cheated because their lovers were better cooks than their wives: 36

"SORRY, DEAR, YOUR KANGAROO SURPRISE MAKES ME FEEL OLD."

Percentage of unfaithful husbands in Australia who say their affairs were motivated by the fear of getting old: 50

perfect figures

*WHY THEY KEEP BUILDING
SUPER 8 HOTELS.*

Odds that a married man
will cheat:
1 in 2.5

Odds that his wife
will cheat:
1 in 8.3

．．．．．．．．．．

E-mail has rewritten the rules of evidence. It is a permanent record of casual remarks, sometimes without the context of a smile or laugh (thus the e-mail convention of emoticons). In many of the cases involving electronic wrongdoing—Microsoft's antitrust case being the most prominent—employers' internal e-mail records have provided legal evidence against them. When sexual harassment is involved, the courts have ruled that an off-color joke distributed by e-mail can contribute to a hostile environment. At many companies, the simple click of a button forwards a message to thousands of people, only one of whom need be outraged. Deleting messages doesn't mean that they go away; they're still in the system and are still accessible to employers.

Even without an actual complaint, a company that actively punishes mischievous e-mailers creates a persuasive defense against future acts of harassment. That's why the body count is so high and why surveillance software sells so well.

Your Boss Is Big Brother

Most of the cases mentioned here involve sexual content. But the judicial panic about racy Internet images obscures a deeper issue: How and when does the right to privacy disappear from our daily work life? Courts have recognized a worker's right to privacy in cases that don't involve online access: Employers generally can't search desks, listen surreptitiously to voice mail, install hidden video cameras, or rifle through personal belongings. The federal wiretap law forbids an employer from listening to a personal phone conversation unless it is done for business reasons and the employee has been notified that his conversations will be monitored (if the employer realizes it's a personal call, he is legally required to end the monitoring).

Computers are a different matter. Since the company owns the machines, the courts reason, it has the right to view anything stored on them, particularly if it has told employees not to use them for personal e-mail or surfing. In the court's view, you give up the expectation of privacy as soon as you log on. In cyberspace, your boss has every right to act like Big Brother.

Zero-tolerance e-mail policies offer employers a quick solution to a thorny legal problem. Companies can protect themselves by installing inexpensive filtering and monitoring software. The technology was originally developed to help parents, teachers, and librarians monitor the surfing and e-mail habits of kids by blocking porn sites and flagging messages that contain "adult" words. Workplace programs such as Mimesweeper, LittleBrother, and Cameo can be unbelievably thorough: Cameo, which can be operated from a desktop computer, checks the text and subject lines of all incoming and outgoing e-mail messages for any of 60 keywords specified by the employer. When a match is found, the message, including attachments, is copied and forwarded to a designated administrator for review. The sender and recipient don't even realize they're being watched.

Employer eavesdropping isn't limited to e-mail messages. A product called Spector takes surreptitious digital screenshots every few seconds of whatever happens to be on an employee's monitor. The manufacturer boasts that it's very much like a surveillance camera. Another program captures every stroke of a keyboard. Employers can also run "drill down" procedures that produce a list of each Web site an employee visits.

That means even a brief visit to a Web site deemed unacceptable can become grounds for dismissal. Once you've sent personal e-mail or peeked at eBay, even for a moment, you're at

SEX ✛ TRENDS

HOW TO NOT GET BUSTED IN THE GREAT OUTDOORS

Good news for Massachusetts vacationers: A new state-police guideline makes it legal to have sex in public—as long as you take a few basic precautions. The rule, announced in March, states that sexual activity in places such as rest areas, beaches, and parks is acceptable as long as it's adequately hidden from view.
In fact, the thrill of having sex under a wide-open sky is more accessible in the rest of the country than you might think. You're almost always safe in a tent. And you're usually safe outside of one as long as you keep mostly covered, stick to secluded areas, and keep the noise down. "Most of the people arrested while having sex in parks are arrested for closure violations— they're there after hours," says Gerry Gaumer, public-affairs specialist with the National Park Service and former law-enforcement official. The rest usually haven't kept themselves covered, so they've violated public-nudity laws—a citation that generally carries a $50 to $100 fine.

the mercy of your employer, who can dredge up any "violation." About 40 percent of American companies use this type of software; it's how Xerox ferreted out the company's 40 offenders.

Surfers who make a point of steering clear of X-rated sites shouldn't make the mistake of thinking that their employer's watchful eye is limited to evidence of sexual harassment. If you use your computer to find health information on your lunch break, to e-mail the pharmacy to fill a prescription, to send your lawyer a note about your divorce, or to take a look at a job site to find out what you should be getting paid, your boss can know about it as soon as you do. Once your fingers touch the keyboard, your expectation of privacy disappears.

As an information-technology manager recently told the *Wall Street Journal*, "You live in a democracy; you don't work in one."

THE FUNNY PAGE

"Well, well, well! If it isn't hanky and panky!"

HELP ONLINE

CATCH HER IN THE ACT

Think your wife may be getting some outside action? Find out for sure with supplies from Spyzone.com. They sell gadgets of every kind— from discreet surveillance cameras and phone lie detectors to tracking systems that reveal where she has driven. "Q" would be proud.

www.spyzone.com

LAWSUIT LOGISTICS

This is a guy-friendly site covering a topic that typically puts us on the defensive: sexual harassment. It separates myth from fact, translates the law into layman's terms, and highlights various sexual-harassment rulings. The site also dedicates an entire section to the topic of men as *victims* of sexual harassment. Not since Clarence Thomas found that hair in his Coke have guys been so well-informed.

www.vix.com/pub/men/harass/harass.html

KEEP YOUR KIDS SAFE

It's 10 o'clock. Do you know where your kids are . . . in cyberspace? With all those porn sites out there (which we've stumbled across accidentally, of course), we know how unsafe the Internet can be for impressionable youngsters. That's where Cyberangels comes in. It's one of the largest online safety and education programs on the 'Net. The group's hundreds of volunteers patrol the World Wide Web for kiddie porn as well as for sites advocating child abuse and pedophilia. Indeed, they've helped put many child pornographers and predators behind bars, making the Internet a safer place for your kids to surf.

www.cyberangels.com

MAN'S GUIDE INTERVIEW

Dating in the Workplace: From the Water Cooler to the Witness Stand

An Interview with Brenton A. Bleier

There was a time not so long ago when sexual-harassment laws didn't even exist. Now, a few high-profile court cases later, many men are reluctant to compliment their female co-workers, let alone pursue a good old-fashioned office romance. The very laws meant to protect women from a "hostile work environment" feel like a threat to guys.

Although the reality of male-female interactions in offices across America is not as grim as some headlines might have you believe, certainly there are risks. For advice on how significant those risks are and how to minimize them, we turned to California attorney Brenton A. Bleier, who authored the article "The Eye of the Beholder: The Subjective Predicate of Sexual Harassment in the '90s" for the February 1995 issue of Legal News *and* Review.

We asked him to translate that title into real-world lingo. And we just hope he won't bill us for time.

MAN'S GUIDE: **Some companies have policies against dating in the workplace, and many others either tacitly or explicitly discourage office romances. Is this much ado about nothing, or is such dating truly a problem?**

BLEIER: I think that it really depends on the relationship between the two people. If we're just talking about two co-workers, the answer is no. That is to say, there isn't any real "problem" from a legal standpoint. There might be some issues and problems from a career standpoint, but that would be it.

So if it's a pair of co-workers, it's pretty much okay. Also, if the guy who is asking the woman out—and let's face it, guys are usually the initiators in dating situations—is subordinate to the woman he's asking, there is also no legal problem.

However, a superior cannot safely date a subordinate. It's virtually impossible to do, from a legal standpoint, without getting into very, very hot water. So, men, listen up: Don't ask out women who are subordinate to you on the company's chain of command. Never.

MAN'S GUIDE: So a man who is brazen enough to ask out a superior at the office, or who gets asked out by her, doesn't have to worry about being dragged into court for it. What about the female superior in that relationship?

BLEIER: She would be putting herself and the company at risk for a lawsuit. Theoretically, if the relationship went south or if the female superior was making unwelcome advances, the man would be able to take her down. It's not the sort of thing you see very often, but the guy could do the same thing many women have done in terms of workplace sexual-harassment cases.

MAN'S GUIDE: What are the risks, legal or otherwise, to the company?

BLEIER: There are a lot of risks for the company when these kinds of relationships go on. And over the past couple years, the U.S. Supreme Court has really broadened the risks that companies face.

For example, there was a big case involving a female lifeguard in Florida who had never once complained about any unwelcome advances while she was on the job. It wasn't until after she left that job on her own that she complained and brought a lawsuit.

You see, that is the real risk from the company's standpoint: They can be nailed at any time. The company may never even see this lawsuit coming. Heck, the woman could have even been happy dating this co-worker of hers. The advances could have been welcomed by her, but it doesn't matter. Her career could go a little sour, she could be fired or laid off, and—like any person of any gender who feels betrayed by the company—might be looking for a way to get back at the organization. And a sexual-harassment case is often a perfect way to do that.

MAN'S GUIDE: Assuming there is ample evidence, I suppose.

BLEIER: Not really. Bringing a case like this is pretty easy. There is no requirement that the woman be damaged in any way. She doesn't have to show that she objected to the dating at the time or that she was denied promotions or anything like that. The woman could have been happy in the relationship at the time, she could have been promoted by the company despite dating a co-worker, and she can still complain later on and have a viable case.

MAN'S GUIDE: So the company could get sued, but it's unlikely that the man will?

BLEIER: Women don't want to sue their current boyfriends—or even ex-boyfriends—over this kind of stuff, most of the time. Mostly because they legitimately don't want to, but also because they aren't likely to get much of an award from the guy in terms of a financial judgment. It's the company that will have the deep pockets in most cases.

MAN'S GUIDE: That being the case, why should the man care whether workplace dating is technically a problem? After all, it's not so much his problem as it is his employer's.

BLEIER: He might be putting his career at risk. Once the woman takes on the employer and says that the dating created a hostile environment and therefore the company is responsible for this—well, this could have serious ramifications for the man's job. That is the part of workplace dating that can sneak up behind you.

MAN'S GUIDE: How do you minimize the risks to yourself and the company—assuming you feel that a woman at work is worth the risk in the first place?

BLEIER: Well, there are a couple rules that I would suggest a man follow if he wants to initiate a dating relationship with a female co-worker.

First, never solicit that date at a company location or on company time. That is very important. If a case is filed, no one can say you lurked at her desk or stalked her through the office or something like that.

Second, don't be talking about the relationship to other employees. If you are dating someone, try to keep that subject outside of the conversations at the office. If the relationship is something that gets talked about at work, it may appear to be inextricably linked up with the work relationship. That could hurt the man if he ends up in court.

Instead of being a situation of "He and I just went out on a few dates," it may become "He talked about me and what we did together in a way that made the work environment hostile and uncomfortable."

MAN'S GUIDE: So, keep the personal and professional separate.

BLEIER: Right. But remember, that's for people who are co-workers. If you are the woman's superior, there is just no way. You just cannot do it safely, no matter how many releases you get her to sign or how much she says "I don't mind if we date" or "If things end for us, I won't take it out on you at work."

Besides, the process of dating is such that there don't tend to be many witnesses around. People are not following the two of you around . . . [to] accurately report back how voluntarily the woman entered into the relationship, how consensual it was, or anything like that.

It isn't just the supervisor who has to be careful. It is worse than that. If you are on a significantly different level than the female at all, you may get into the danger zone. Let's say you are a vice president in a large company and you don't actively supervise the woman in question. In fact, let's say you are in a completely different department in a completely different building. That is still too hard to defend, because you are considered a company representative.

If there is a lawsuit, the employee who is doing the "harassing" by asking her out—this hypothetical manager or executive in another part of the organization—is an official representative of the company in dealings with the woman. It won't really matter that she's not in his chain of command.

MAN'S GUIDE: Not a pretty picture.

BLEIER: Long ago there was a saying: Don't dip your pen in the company inkwell.

MAN'S GUIDE: Unless you want your pen—and your pair of paperweights—handed to you on a platter.

BLEIER: There is a reason that such a saying existed even before sexual harassment became an official legal issue. Dating women in the workplace was a practice that was just too risky to your career.

The first thing a guy should do, if he is even thinking about asking out a co-worker, is to get out the company hand-book to see what the rules of the company are in this regard. He needs to abide by company policy. If you are reading the handbook and you have questions, talk to your superior or to someone in the human resources division. Otherwise, by dating a fellow worker, you may have just jeopardized your career. It's a minefield.

perfect figures

OF COURSE, THIS ALSO INCLUDES NBA PLAYERS.

Percentage of people who have more than one sex partner at the same time: 34

. . . .

MAN'S GUIDE: **Guys across America are going to have to put off those plans to ask out the cute blonde in accounting or the tall brunette in word processing. Hopes are being dashed even as we speak.**

Why does it have to be this way?

BLEIER: One reason this can get so hairy is that dating relationships are what I would call a he-said-she-said situation. Let's face it, most people don't take notes about dates and their relationships. So the woman can bring a case years later and say that this happened and that happened. The court will assume she can prove—or at least back up—the issues and events about which she is complaining.

MAN'S GUIDE: **You suggest that harassment laws are unfair. Just how un-fair are they?**

BLEIER: It seems to me, in this world today—especially if you buy into the politically correct nature of our times—such laws are pro-foundly unnecessary and even patronizing to women. If women are going to hold all the same kinds of jobs as men do, and do all the same things that men can do, they should be able to speak up right away and simply tell a guy, "No, I really don't want to go out with you."

In the old days—before these sexual-harassment laws were even a notion—when women were mostly in subordinate positions, there was probably a need for this kind of extra protection. But what we have now is stacked in favor of the accusers so heavily that it is ripe for fraudulent accusations and fraudulent cases.

MAN'S GUIDE: It sounds like the man is pretty much hosed if a woman accuses him of sexual harassment.

BLEIER: The problem is that the basis for the case can be built on completely subjective information and statements. Unfortunately, the penalties—the financial judgments—are very concrete. A company cannot insure itself against this sort of thing, so it cannot afford to take the risk of going to trial in most cases. Therefore, a lot of these cases get settled out of court.

Now, the guy who asked the woman out is in Dutch with his employers because he "caused" all the problems. From the company's standpoint, it's really his fault that lawyers had to be hired, all this hassle had to be endured, and all that money paid out to the plaintiff.

This is a really unusual area of law. In fact, it is the only area of the law that I know of in which one party can change his or her mind about a situation after the fact, and that altered perception becomes the actual basis of the "crime."

MAN'S GUIDE: Before we know it, we'll have to have attorneys on retainer to go with us on our dates.

BLEIER: One of the big things that has really changed is that sexual harassment has split into two different areas. One is the quid-pro-quo situation, in which something work-related is provided in return for the dating relationship. That could be anything from promising a promotion to saying, "You can only keep your job if you date me."

But more and more, we have been faced with a second type of harassment, in which you might not have said or done anything distasteful or unethical but the woman simply complains that your attention was unwelcome. Well, the question there is, how would a man know the request for a date was unwelcome until he asked? And what really qualifies as "unwelcome" behavior? It is a really fuzzy area.

This is why you should take it outside the workplace, and never talk about your dating life at work.

MAN'S GUIDE: Is there anything else preemptive or protective you can do?

BLEIER: There isn't much more you can do to minimize the risks than what I have already outlined. I mean, theoretically, you could drag her in front of a third party and read her some dating version of the Miranda rights.

MAN'S GUIDE: That would be trippy, eh? "You have the right to refuse to go out on a date with me. If you choose to exercise that right, there will be no recriminations. If you choose to waive that right, you agree that you will not take me or my company to court for sexual harassment." That's sure to get you a wild-and-crazy dream date.

BLEIER: Yes, I do believe an extreme measure like that would end the relationship before it even began. Not very romantic.

MAN'S GUIDE: Is there any way around workplace dating? With professional people, in particular, they spend so many hours at the office now, it seems like the best place to shop for love. Fewer and fewer people seem to have lives outside work.

BLEIER: I think you are right. It's true in large part because of the disintegration of other dating alternatives in our society. It seems like every radio station now has some kind of dating-database thing going, in which they match people up. Why are people reduced to this sort of thing? Simple: They have no place else to go. If you don't want to go to singles bars, there are not many other places to go.

So the average guy will often think to himself, even if he knows the risks of workplace dating, "I'll just roll the dice."

MAN'S GUIDE: . . . And hope it isn't snake eyes.

BLEIER: It is true that most people who engage in these relationships are taking a risk, and they may be well-aware of that risk. Fact is, we all take lots of risks in life, like driving cars.

The troubling thing, though, is that most of our risks in life are not subjectively based, like the current harassment laws. Let's face it: People have been known to change their minds for lots of reasons. But if a woman you work with changes her mind about how she views your dating relationship with her, she can create awful havoc for you.

And if you are fired for something like this, you can become a pariah in the work world. You can become almost unemployable because companies open themselves up to too much risk and liability if something like that should happen again with another woman. So again, I cannot emphasize this enough: Make the dating arrangements outside of the company, and don't talk about those dates at the office.

QUICKIES

PLAYING AWAY MAKES YOU BETTER AT HOME

If she's not buying the old cross-dressing line, here's the perfect excuse for that stray pair of panties down the back of the sofa: having an affair makes you a better husband, according to Italian researchers. The study, published in the journal *Psychology and Communication*, found that the guilt of affairs drove men to be more affectionate to their wives, spending 20 percent more time with them, paying more attention to their own appearance, and doing extra jobs around the house.

As for the reasons behind their dalliances, more than 50 percent said they were reacting to a fear of getting old, while 36 percent claimed they fell for women who cooked tastier food.

However mouthwatering the prospect may be, here's a warning: Affairs are one of the biggest factors in divorce. And even if it doesn't go that far, the relationship could be changed forever.

The Italian researchers were too busy arguing over custody of their CD collections to comment.

HOW TO HAVE A ONE-NIGHT STAND WITHOUT MAKING A MESS

It turns out there is such a thing as bad sex. In a study of 33 men and women ages 25 to 52, Norwegian researchers found that 30 had had at least one "negative sexual experience"—usually a one-night stand, usually involving alcohol. When the subjects told the researchers the dirty details of their encounters, a few common themes emerged. If you're going to have a one-nighter, follow these rules.

● Don't have sex with someone you know.
A key component of the successful one-night stand is not having to see the other person again. If you share a cubicle, a car pool, or play bridge together every Wednesday night, you'll quickly get in over your head. That goes double for folks in the office: Sleeping with someone you work with is the kiss of death to your confidence in weekly meetings, according to the study participants.

● Don't let your beer do the talking.
Even if you've been drinking, take a minute to step back and observe the situation as an outsider. Is this really somebody you'd be talking to if you were

sober? If you're already feeling the first twinges of embarrassment, it's only going to get worse. Pass.

● Don't assume the encounter means something.
Surprisingly, the study found that men were actually more likely than women to feel guilty and hurt after realizing a one-night stand lacked emotional significance. If you're not sure what she wants from you, ask.

● Be wild in bed.
If it's going to be purely about sex, make sure it's worth it. The more fun you have, the more you'll look back fondly on your night of passion—and at least feel like you got something good out of it. Concentrate on her pleasure first (the more she enjoys herself, the more you will) and on techniques that delay ejaculation. Change positions frequently and make a lot of noise.

TWO WORDS THAT MIGHT GET YOU SUED FOR SEXUAL HARASSMENT

Monica Lewinsky.

A judge ruled that a sexual-harassment lawsuit filed by a college student against a professor could proceed because the professor repeatedly called her by the name of the former White House intern.

Inbal Hayut, a former student at the State University of New York at New Paltz, said remarks by the professor, Alex Young, created a "sexually hostile environment." The professor, who later retired, made comments such as "Shut up, Monica. I'll give you a cigar later," according to court records.

At least the professor didn't insist that Hayut take an oral exam.

ASK THE SEX DOC

Q: *Is there a way to tell if the personnel department has been snooping around in my office e-mail?*
—B. B., Wichita, Kansas

A: Think of your e-mails at work the same way you'd think of yourself in the shower without a curtain: fully exposed. While it's legal for companies to rummage through your messages without your knowing, it's hard to detect when they do it. A tip-off: your system asks for a new password, says Richard Bliss, a messaging security specialist in California. It could mean that someone deleted your old password to gain access to your account. Suspicious?

Delete and clear your trash of anything you regret sending. "Companies usually back up the system at the end of every day, so if you delete it before 5 o'clock, there's a good chance it won't be saved," says Bliss.

Avoid profane or sexual language. Consider it an invitation to be flagged.

Change passwords often. This makes it harder for others to gain access.

Use a private e-mail address for personal stuff. Accounts such as Hotmail can be accessed from work but are harder for employers to track.

Q: *My wife caught me masturbating over porn recently and has been moody with me ever since.* How do I get out of this one?
—M. K., Decatur, Georgia

A: Not by saying, "Get a load of this centerfold." The trick is to bring the subject out into the open.

First of all, you need to work out whether it's the masturbation or the porn that bothers her. If it's both, tackle each topic in separate conversations.

If it's your masturbation she's worried about, try to get her to see that it's simply a harmless way of satisfying an urge. Most men masturbate, even when they're in relationships. They see it as a supplement to sex, not a replacement for it.

If she's appalled at the fact that you're ogling images she thinks degrade women, it's more serious. She may feel rejected, and trying to justify your actions may make matters worse. You're better off reassuring her that she's desirable and trying to make her understand that your feelings about porn are separate from your feelings about her. Then your options are simple: You either give up the porn or find a more secure place to look at it.

The Sex Doc is a fictional character.
The actual advice was provided by a variety of
medical doctors and other qualified experts.

8

SPOT-CHECK
CYBERSEX

Judging by the e-mail we get, cyberspace is full of lusty cheerleaders, horny lesbians, women who have sex with animals, and men who have recently added 6 inches to the length of their penises. It's a place where your wildest fantasies can come true. Assuming, of course, that you can find your way past all the pop-ups and come-ons, want to send your credit-card number to pornographers, and don't mind your fantasy taking shape in a jerky, 2-inch-square window.

Our advice: If you want to use the Internet for sex, skip the seamy world of electronic pornography and go where real people are making connections. Find yourself a chat room, personals site, or erotic Webzine and conduct yourself the way you would in the real world. Use today's technology (and tomorrow's) the same way you used yesterday's. Send sexy e-mails instead of love letters. Have cybersex instead of phone sex. You get the idea.

Used correctly, it works. You can meet people, develop relationships, even build something of a sex life—all without taking your hands off the keyboard. (Well, you may want to free up one hand.) In this section, we offer a few suggestions for finding romance in that vast universe of bytes and pixels.

TOP TEN

Ways to Tell If Someone Is Lying in Cyberspace

In cyberspace, no one knows for sure who anyone really is. You could be chatting with a 67-year-old grandmother. Or a 12-year-old girl. Or an Iowa farm boy. All of whom purport to be a Heidi Klum look-alike.

More 'Net users are mousing around with their identities than you might expect. A poll of 9,000 Web users conducted by California sex researcher Al Cooper found that 60 percent had fibbed about their age, and 40 percent had lied about their race. "Gender bending" was much less widespread: Only 5 percent admitted to switching sexes online.

For some, not knowing who's on the other end of the modem is part of the allure. For others, it's decidedly not. If you'd rather be assured that xStaci really is the blonde babe she claims to be, follow these tips for spotting a cyberdisguise.

1 **Stay away from sex sites.** Look for a companion on a general-interest site rather than a site or chat room geared toward romance, dating, or cybersex. Folks frequenting general sites have little reason to lie about their identities or make themselves out to be better than they are.

2 **Look out for exaggeration or embellishment.** If someone's story sounds unbelievable, it probably is. Would someone who looked like Heidi Klum really be trolling cyberspace for dates?

3 **Consider names.** Don't assume that unisex monikers like Terry, Pat, Shannon, Robin, or Devon actually belong to women. You never know who's using an ambiguous name with anything but ambiguous intentions.

4 **Ask for a *.gif.*** That's a picture, in cyberese.

5 **Seek live contact.** Ask to speak on the phone or meet face-to-face. If they're lying about their identities, they'll make excuses and put you off.

6 **Spot slipups.** Be on the lookout for inconsistencies in the person's story. If "she" is spinning an elaborate lie, it's bound to trip "her" up at some point.

7 **Don't throw anything away.** Keep prior e-mails or transcripts of chats to look back on later. That way, you don't have to rely on your memory to spot inconsistencies.

8 **Watch for cyberpauses.** If you're chatting with the person in real time, look out for any delay or hesitation. Your e-pal may be taking more time to respond in order to think through a "story" before sharing it with you.

9 **Ask key questions.** Pose a question to which only a woman would likely know the correct response. Here's one way to do it: Tell your cyberdate you spotted a gift you'd like to mail her. Just to keep her guessing, ask for her clothing size, ring size, or even panty-hose size. If she's truly a "she," she'll know that women's clothing sizes range from size 2 on up, that women typically wear ring sizes 5 through 7, and that panty hose comes in sizes A, B, and Queen.

10 **Look for typos.** Researchers at the University of Texas in Austin found that men in chat rooms tended to correct their typing more often than women.

MUST READS

Getting Personal with Personal Ads

You're a complex human being. You have a unique personality, a specific look, hopes, dreams, goals, preferences, tastes. You have opinions, hobbies, a career, a family, a religion, a political party. Now sum all that up in 30 words or less. Yow! Tricky, isn't it? We had a hard time, too, and we're editors. If you're going to bother with the hassle (and maybe the expense) of posting a personal ad, do something that 99 percent of guys don't: Put a little thought into it. In this excerpt from The Complete Idiot's Guide to Online Dating and Relating *(Que Corporation, 2000), Joe Schwartz tells you how.*

The biggest mistake people make when writing their personal ads is creating one while they are online at the Web site they plan to list it on. A cursory exploration of the online-ad terrain will display oodles of ads that begin with variations on "I really don't know what to say" and "I'm not used to writing about myself." I suggest you read through the tips that follow, type up your ad in advance on your word processor, and then when you place your ad, copy the text onto the Web site's registration form.

Choose an Identity Carefully

Almost every Web site that lists personals will require you to use a handle or alias so you can receive e-mails from interested parties without revealing your name. The choice of what your pseudonym will be is a key decision for your personal ad as it is usually the first thing your prospective respondents will see and will announce a great deal about your personality or desires. Here are some tips to choosing your perfect handle:

● Make it meaningful.

It is always amazing to me how often a person's handle will be something generic like "Girl1024" or "WorkingGuy34." Not only do these examples tell very little about the writer other than gender (and in WorkingGuy's case, that he might not have a lot of time to spare), but the number usually suggests that there is nothing particularly special about the writer because there are dozens of others using an almost identical handle.

One way to give your handle meaning is to make an easily recognizable connection to some activity or pursuit you participate in. For example, TennisFiend clearly likes to volley and serve, while BronteLover has an affinity for

Charlotte, Emily, and Anne Brontë, three sisters who wrote poetry and prose in the 1800s. What's particularly nice about using this method is that you not only announce a life passion but also dissuade people who do not share your interest from contacting you. Of course, you should only use this method for creating a handle if you have a true passion for something.

Another way to make it meaningful is to create a handle that contains a slightly obscure reference or inside joke. For example, FeathersMcGraw could be a handle for someone who loves the Wallace and Gromit animated films. People who've seen *The Wrong Trousers*, the film in which this character appears, would get the reference immediately, while others might read the personal ad just based on the handle's novelty. A side benefit to choosing a handle this way is that it can often start a conversation when people ask you what your handle refers to.

❶ Be descriptive.

There's no doubt that men and women can be visually stimulated. A good descriptive handle can start that process even before Web surfers gaze upon your countenance. PerkyBlonde or MarlboroMan tell us that the former is probably a woman (men don't often describe themselves as perky) who is an energetic and fun-loving blonde. The latter is a guy's guy: rugged, individualistic, and solid. Be aware, though, that depending on what associations come to the mind of the reader, your descriptive ad might be taken the wrong way. The PerkyBlonde could be thought of as annoying, while the MarlboroMan might be mistaken for a heavy smoker. Fortunately, you can always explain your handle further in the actual personal ad.

❶ Be suggestive.

The difference between a handle that's descriptive and one that's suggestive is the descriptive ad says something about the way you look, act, or run your life, while the suggestive one implies a goal or course of action. HoldMyHand is a handle that might suggest this person is looking for affection and companionship, while WildRide might be implying the need for a more physically active relationship. If you decide to use a suggestive handle, and especially if you don't, be careful that you don't unintentionally create a double entendre.

> " I'd been downloaded 75,000 times in 24 hours. I didn't even know what a download was. "
>
> —Internet sex kitten Cindy Margolis, on the first time her picture hit cyberspace

Create an Attention-Grabbing Headline

Many personal ad sites require you to compose a headline for your ad. This is important not only as an introduction to the ad itself, but because many sites initially provide surfers with only a list of ad headlines. If someone likes your headline, he or she might then click a link and view your entire ad.

Just as you might do for your handle, you can use your headline to describe yourself or what you're looking for. Most probably though, the personal ad Web site has a search function that guides the person looking at your headline to see a list of headlines based on gender, age, geographic location, and a host of other factors. As such, you could also use your headline to draw attention to your ad by amplifying some aspect of your personality or by just being playful. Here are some examples of headlines that fall into this category.

YES, I'D LOVE SOME WINE. THANK YOU.

THE STORE SHELVES ARE ALL EMPTY. WAIT, THERE'S ONE LEFT!

SHE LOOKED LIKE TROUBLE. WELL, MAYBE THAT'S WHAT I WAS IN THE MARKET FOR.

GET ME SOME CHEEZIPOOFS!

PICK ME! PICK ME!

Honestly Describe Yourself and What You're Looking For

There is no greater letdown than meeting face-to-face with someone you've interacted with online and finding out that she was less than truthful in describing her appearance. The same is true when you find out your date who professed a love for all your passions really just wanted to sound accommodating. Though we always want to show ourselves in a positive light, it is essential that your ad be truthful. Don't, for instance, say you're muscular when you're actually slight of build. Not everyone wants a bodybuilder, and people are always happier when they feel they've been dealt with honestly.

This rule becomes doubly important when you're writing what you want in regards to a relationship and the person you're looking for. For instance, if you're just looking for sex, you should

hot TIP!

Women snoop. For that matter, so do children and roommates and, we're almost certain, cats. If you don't want anyone checking your e-mail, get yourself a private account and change your password regularly.

say so to attract people with a similar goal. This doesn't mean you have to write "I only want sexual relationships" (although there's nothing wrong with this), but it does mean being clear in your goals. If someone who only wants sex states something to the effect of "I'm only looking for short-term relationships and to have some fun," this at least tells those people who are looking for committed relationships to move on.

Reveal Something about Yourself

When people create their personal ads, they usually list activities and pursuits that they are involved in. There is definitely a place for some of this information in your ad, but a laundry list of things you do does not necessarily make you or your ad interesting. Personal revelations concerning your life, how you feel about things, the way you think, and just quirky observations will reveal your personality and thus make the ad more representative of who you are. I'm not saying you should reveal deeply moving or traumatic events from your life, but you should try to differentiate yourself from the other ads by showing that there is a real person behind the writing. Some examples of personal revelations in online ads are:

> "I like to walk on the beach. I feel at home near the water."

> "Have you noticed how all the ATMs now charge you a buck or more if you don't have an account at that particular bank? Well, I remember when it was free and if it bothers you as much as me, perhaps we should talk."

> "Pancakes are a favorite food of mine. My mother used to make them for me as a child, and they're still my favorite comfort food."

> "My friends say I'm too picky. Well, it's important to me to be picky when I'm looking for someone to spend my life with."

Create a Little Mystery

To paraphrase the old saw, a person ceases to be interesting when all mystery is lost. So how do you cultivate mystery in a personal ad while still being open and forthright about your description, goals, and desires? One way is to reveal only part of a fact with the hope that learning the rest will pique someone's interest. For example, if you've traveled throughout Europe, you could state in your ad that you've "traveled extensively" (which would be too general), list every country you've been to, or say something like "I've visited the homes of five different European rulers." If someone who shares your interest in travel reads the latter, it might get them to write to you to find out what countries you've been to and to learn more about your adventurous spirit.

Another way to create mystery is to ask questions or pose a playful challenge. "Can anyone help me with this crossword? I need a five-letter word for pungent," would announce to the online personal ad community that you love crossword puzzles and are looking for someone to share this interest with. It also creates mystery for other crossword puzzle aficionados who can't figure out what the five-letter word is. (For those who can't stand a mystery, the answer I was looking for is *acrid*.)

It is important to note that in both the previous stratagems, you do not want to deceive anyone, just pique their interest. And even more important, to pique the interest not of the general population but of those who might be compatible with you.

perfect figures

THEY'RE A SORRY BUNCH,
OUR CO-WORKERS.

Percentage of Internet users surveyed who are addicted to cybersex: 6

Be Specific

I have a friend who, for anonymity's sake, we'll call Henry. Henry is 5 feet 9 inches in height. Henry considers himself tall. When he writes to women over the Internet, they are often upset to find out that he is not over 6 feet in height. Why? Because when they wrote their ads, they used a phrase similar to "Please be tall." Had they written "Please be over 6-feet tall," this hilarity could have been avoided.

Be Positive

It is almost impossible to peruse personal ads on Web sites without running into those that lay out the type of person not wanted. "If you are a loser, do not write me," is typical of these ads. Let's examine the word *loser*. Now, you and I know who all the losers are, but I've rarely known a loser who admits to being one. In fact, many of the losers think that you and I are losers. So despite this admonition, many of the losers end up writing personal ads to those who would rather not be contacted by them.

A better way to approach your ad is to be positive and, again, specifically state what you do want in the person you are trying to meet. It is the difference between writing negatively "No Smokers, please!" and stating positively "Please be a nonsmoker."

Common Personal Ad Pitfalls to Avoid

Now that we've discussed some of the ways to make your personal ad effective, let's quickly look at some pitfalls you should try to avoid while writing it.

● The laundry list

Although we are all complex human beings with wide and varied interests, there's no reason you need to put every one of them in your ad. Here's an excerpt from a typical laundry-list ad.

> *A little about me. I enjoy skiing, tennis, baseball, basketball, traveling (I've been to Europe twice!), my job, movies, good books, TV sitcoms, all types of music, spending time with my close friends and family, eating at new restaurants, comedy clubs, going to the theater (Broadway, off-Broadway, cabaret), singing, shopping, long walks on the beach, watching the sunset, talking about everything from art to politics, animals, volunteering, sailing, a night on the town, and quiet evenings at home.*

Now, I have no doubt this person does enjoy all these things, but there is no sense of who he is other than a busy person who likes everything life has to offer with the possible exception of breathing (and I'm only guessing that because it was one of the few things not on the list). I would suggest to this person that he pick the four or five activities that mean the most to him and briefly elaborate on them—because as we'll see in the next paragraph, the laundry list is the flip side of another pitfall.

● Long-windedness

My 10th-grade English teacher was fond of endlessly quoting Polonius's famous line from Shakespeare's *Hamlet*, ". . . brevity is the soul of wit." I'm willing to bet that she would have written a kick-ass personal ad. She knew that it's easy to lose your audience by listing dozens of pieces of minutia. Obviously, if your personal has very little or no information, it will probably not attract much, or the desired, attention, so it's important to strike a balance. Still, it's always good to keep in mind my teacher's other famous cliché, "less is more."

● Subjectivity

I've heard personal ads described as "a form of bragging." But the fact is that only the poorly written personal ads are of a boastful and often empty nature, while the truthful ones are usually the most interesting. There is no better example of this than when someone tries to describe themselves objectively with subjective terms. "I've got a great sense of humor" is one of these phrases. But what does that mean? I probably laugh at different things than you, and both of us might find very unfunny what a third person laughs at uproariously. The point is, rather than just write "I've got a great sense of humor," actually display your sense of humor in the ad. Make a wry comment, tell a joke, or reference comedians you like. Other examples of this type of bragging include "I'm very successful," "Women find me attractive," and "I'm a normal person."

❍ "It's raining cats and dogs on my personal!"

Although it has always been a mainstay of good writing to avoid clichés, the proliferation of personal ads has created a subset of clichés that are common to these ads. They include:

"I'll try anything once! Well, almost anything."

"I'm comfortable in black tie or jeans."

". . . a night on the town or quiet evenings at home."

"I'm a complete package."

Any reference to the words *soul mate*.

Any reference to your mother.

As always, using a cliché will not make your ad an egregious eyesore, but the more you can avoid commonly used phrases, the more successful you'll be at differentiating your ad from the rest.

❍ Self-doubt

Dating books through the decades have extolled the virtues of confidence. The beauty of a personal ad is that you don't have to summon up the brave face you might require meeting someone in person. All you have to do is make sure you don't sound unsure in your ad. Phrases like "I'm not sure what I'm doing here" and "I really feel odd writing this" only detract from your ad. It is a given that most people would rather not have to advertise for their personal or romantic needs. However, if you sound like you're comfortable with the personal ad process, that will make you all the more attractive to others, even those who are unsure themselves. And after you start communicating with someone else, imagine how three-dimensional, not to mention human, you'll appear admitting that you are not totally at ease with the online personal ad process.

❍ YELLING

No one likes to be screamed at, which is what typing in all caps represents on the Internet. Just as sentences written in all capital letters are considered of-

How's Your Personal Ad Doing?

The life span of an online personal ad can vary, but on average, it will certainly be in circulation longer than those that would appear in a printed publication. As a result, you might want to revise your ad from time to time. Use this handy checklist to review what elements you want to keep or revise in a personal ad you've already written.

☐ Is my handle meaningful, descriptive, suggestive, or memorable?

☐ Does my ad headline grab a person's attention?

☐ Do I describe myself honestly?

☐ Have I honestly related what I'm looking for?

☐ Have I revealed something of myself as a person?

☐ Did I create any mystery?

☐ Is the ad specific?

☐ Is the ad positive?

☐ Did I avoid making the ad into a laundry list?

☐ Is the ad filled with enough information to say what's important, but brief enough so that people aren't intimidated by its length?

☐ Did I avoid describing myself objectively with subjective terms (for example, "I have a great sense of humor")?

☐ Did I abstain from using clichés (especially those common to online personal ads)?

☐ Did I eschew sentences written entirely in capital letters?

☐ Is the tone of the ad confident?

fensive in e-mails and other online communications, the same is true for your personal ad. Also, it is often very hard to read ads written this way.

Reading and Replying to Other Ads

The last pitfall to avoid actually concerns responding to other people's ads. Many personals will contain specific requests for what the writer is looking for from others. Although you might have a strong wish to connect with someone, you should always read other ads carefully and abide by the writer's wishes. For example, someone might be looking for a partner who practices a particular religion. Despite the fact that you believe you are a perfect match, unless you plan to also practice that religion, move on and do not respond to the ad.

Everything You Ever Wanted to Know about Sex . . . Is Just a Click Away

Enter the word sex *in a search engine and you'll get tens of millions of hits—most of which lead nowhere. Even more specific queries are often useless. Considering how much we like talking about sex, it seems few of us have anything useful to say. When Michael Castleman set out to learn why, he got a lot more than he bargained for. This is his essay from Salon.com.*

"We live in a culture obsessed with sex," says San Francisco sex authority Sandor Gardos, a sex-advice columnist for ThriveOnline. "But basic sexuality information often gets lost. It's difficult to assign meaningful blame. Sure, the government, parents, political conservatives, and the media deserve some share of it, but we also have thousands of years of cultural history that got us to this point."

In Gardos's view, one hopeful development for increasing access to information about sexuality is the Web: "For the first time ever, people with Web access are only a few clicks away from at least some good sex information. Before the Web, if you were a teen in a small, conservative town, or gay, or a fetishist of some sort, it may have been very difficult to find the information you were looking for. [Now] you can ask your questions, find people like you. People submit questions anonymously, but from the way they're written, I'd guess that about half come from teens. I think that's why I get so many questions asking, 'Could I be pregnant?'"

Gardos is painfully aware that the Web is no treasure trove of authoritative sex information. Far from it. "When I got involved with About.com, one of the first things I did was survey the Web for sources of good sex information. I was surprised at how few I found. There are hundreds of thousands of porn sites, but I found only a few dozen sites with comprehensive sex information, and a few dozen more with good information about specific subject areas: contraception, sexually transmitted diseases,

> ## *hot* TIP!
>
> *Getting turned down by every woman you ask out? Search your own name online. You may find some bozo in a public chat room who shaves his privates . . . and shares your name.*

blow jobs. Still, if you have no other access to good sex information, the Web can provide it—if you know where to look."

The Web has done something for sex-advice columnists too—it's changed the kinds of questions they get. "Questions that come in by e-mail tend to be more intelligent, more literate," says Chip Rowe, who launched PlayboyAdvisor.com in 1997. The Web site now accounts for two-thirds of the letters he receives. "Most people with computers and Web access have a certain level of education—even if they don't know much about sex."

Nationally syndicated sex columnist Isadora Alman agrees: "I get more intelligent questions on the [Sexuality Forum] Web site." Her site is unique in that she's not the sole expert. She invites site visitors to answer questions as well as ask them—in part to provide perspectives other than her own and in part to have her site function as a kind of sexuality salon, an ongoing discussion group. She has found her approach something of an antidote to one occupational hazard of writing a sex-advice column—the feeling that the whole world is sexually out to lunch. "Many people write in wonderful answers," she says. And, in fact, Alman's latest book, *Doing It: Real People Having Really Good Sex* is a compilation of visitors' tips and experiences.

> **" Computers are like pornography. You can't keep them out, so you let users have a belly full until they get things back in perspective. "**
>
> —Michael O'Neill

Everyone's Talking about It

All the sex-advice columnists interviewed for this article have noticed an increased interest in recent years in power-play sex like sadomasochism, bondage and discipline. If the volume of questions related to power-play sex is any indication, it's practiced more and more widely. "Whether or not people are actively involved in S&M and B&D, interest seems to be growing," Alman says. "People have heard of it. They're curious about it. So they ask. And when so many people ask, you have to figure that at least some of them are trying it."

For Alman, whose readers span a broad range of age and sexual experience, S&M and B&D have replaced previous sexual practices once considered "edgy." "Twenty-five years ago, it was oral sex," she explains. "Ten years ago, it was anal. Now it's S&M and B&D." But Rowe's Playboy readers tend to be under 30, and despite Playboy's anything-goes image, they're generally not that sexually adventurous. "Based on the letters I receive," Rowe says, "I'd say anal is still on the edge for most of our readers."

Only one subject has dropped off the sex-advice columnists' radar screens: AIDS. The reason, they speculate, is that HIV transmission is one of the few sexual subjects that have been addressed widely in the mainstream media. The columnists continue to receive a steady stream of questions about other sexually transmitted diseases.

Speaking of old standbys, everything Americans asked about 40 years ago, they're still asking about today: questions dealing with penis size, premature ejaculation, inability to reach orgasm, losing one's virginity, abortion, contraception, the G spot. Is it okay to masturbate? How can I meet someone? Why does he watch so much porn? How can I get my partner to try something new in bed? And any number of fantasies or experiences that end with "So, what do you think; am I normal?"

Playboy Advisor's Rowe says, "The word *normal* can be tricky. In a sexual context, it has several meanings: popular, safe, nothing to feel ashamed of. Plenty of things are safe and nothing to feel ashamed of, even if they are not all that popular. Instead of *normal*, I try to go with *safe* or *unhealthy*, *common* or *uncommon*. So much of what I do is give people permission to be themselves, to enjoy who they are."

The Web has also enabled people around the world to ask more questions. The vast majority still come from Americans, but Alman has received quite a few from abroad: "Most come from the U.K., presumably because my site is in English, but I've had questions from Europe, Asia, and South America," she says. Alman thought Europeans would be more sexually sophisticated than Americans

SEX TRENDS

EFFECTS OF COMPUTERIZED SEX

Along with the advent of interactive pornography came the concern that men able to routinely "control" virtual females might develop unhealthy attitudes toward real-life women. But a study from the University of Western Ontario suggests that you can surf all you want without threatening your real-life relationship. After observing 100 men interacting with three different computerized sex shows, the researchers concluded that men's attitudes toward an intentionally provocative female research assistant remained unchanged. Yes, but, what about their wives?

are, but she says that has not been the case. "It's the same old stuff, especially questions from men about coming too soon."

Gardos also receives questions from abroad. The only difference he's noticed is that foreign women are more likely to ask a question like "How can I be sure I bleed on my wedding night?" (This question reflects ignorance about the hymen, the membrane that supposedly covers a virgin's vagina.) "In many countries around the world," he explains, "sex information is more suppressed than it is here, so you'd expect more people to have more basic questions."

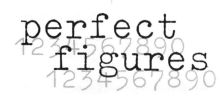

perfect figures

WILL A CONDOM ON YOUR MONITOR PREVENT COMPUTER VIRUSES, TOO?

Percentage of Internet users surveyed who report having had an online affair: 42

Someone's Gotta Do It

The columnists estimate that 80 to 90 percent of the questions they receive are ones they've seen before. They live for the 10 to 20 percent that are new and different. "Just when I think I've seen it all," Gardos says, "I get a question that makes me say, 'Wow, I've never heard of that.'"

Recently, a man asked whether it was safe to scuba dive with a hydraulic penile implant, whether the extra pressure underwater might cause his implant to malfunction. "I had no idea," Gardos admits. "None of my books had anything on it. So I called all over the place—sex people, dive shops—and finally wound up talking to people at the company that had manufactured the guy's implant. They'd never considered the scuba question either. But based on other tests they'd run, they guessed that their implant would work fine down to about 100 feet. I wrote him back saying that no one really knew the answer, but I told him what the manufacturer had said."

"In the 17 years I've been doing my column," Alman says, "I've never been bored. Amused, amazed, saddened, distressed, fascinated, and titillated, but never bored."

"My fondest wish is to work myself out of a job," Gardos says. "But until that happens—and I don't think there's any chance it ever will—I have fun giving sex advice. It's a service many people clearly need."

"Sometimes I laugh out loud at amazing or witty stories," says OnHealth sex advisor Louanne Weston, a sex therapist in Fair Oaks, California. "And I really love getting thank-you notes. That happens fairly frequently. Recently, I wrote a piece on the fact that some blood pressure medications cause erection impairment. I got a note from a woman saying that because of my column, her impotent husband asked his doctor to change his blood pressure medication, and now they're enjoying sex again. That kind of feedback makes my day."

"I can't think of a better job than being the Playboy Advisor," Rowe says. "I have an office full of sex books and porn. I'm always learning new things about sex. And maybe something I write helps someone become more self-accepting, or have a better relationship, or more fun in bed. What else do you need?"

Will Cybersex Be Better Than Real Sex?

With few exceptions, every prediction ever made about the future has been wrong. Remember George Orwell's 1984? *What about all those wacky gizmos exhibited at various World's Fairs? So we don't give much credence to folks who try to convince us that any day now we'll be having realistic and satisfying sex over the Internet. Writer Joel Stein road-tested a prototype cybersex apparatus for* Time *magazine, and he agrees.*

There are two fields in which I'm anxious to see technology improve: medicine and hard-core pornography. And since I'm not sick yet, I'm pretty focused on the porn thing. Luckily, I am not alone in my stunted vision of utopia. The desire for newer, better smut has long been a major impetus behind technological progress: VCRs, DVDs, Web development, and I believe x-ray glasses were all spurred by prurient desires.

The holy grail of pornography, though, has always been a machine that delivers a virtual experience so real that it is indistinguishable from sex, other than the fact that it isn't at all disappointing. Though prototypes have appeared in films (the Pleasure Organ in *Barbarella*, the Orgasmatron in *Sleeper*, the fembots in *Austin Powers*), reality has remained painfully elusive. In his 1991 book *Virtual Reality*, Howard Rheingold devoted an entire chapter to "teledildonics," his not-so-clever name for devices that allow people to have sex without being in the same area code. Rheingold imagines putting on a "diaphanous bodysuit, something like a body stocking but with the kind of intimate snugness of a condom" and having a virtual-reality sexperience over the 'Net. "You run your hand over your partner's clavicle and 6,000 miles away, an array of effectors are triggered, in just the right sequence, at just the right frequency, to convey the touch exactly the way you wish it to be conveyed."

Other than his fetish for Chinese clavicle, Rheingold is able to provide little that's useful in the way of information or specs. And in the 9 years since he published his personal fantasies, there has been surprisingly little progress. Vivid, the world's largest producer of adult entertainment, promised to deliver an interactive bodysuit a couple of years ago but missed its deadline. Sure, it had a $200,000 black neoprene suit with 36 electrodes stuck to the chest, crotch, and other special places, but the suit didn't look very appetizing. Nor did it do anything. Vivid says it's waiting for FCC approval (interaction with pacemakers seems to be a concern), but the real reason it is lying low on the sex suit is that Vivid is a proud company, and it's not going to continue trumpeting a technology that is at best a long way from happening.

But there are less proud pornographers. SafeSexPlus.com sells teledildonic devices that, it turns out, look a lot like dildonic devices. The company promised that if I used these gizmos in conjunction with their iFriends.net Web site, I could have a sexual experience over the 'Net. I got SafeSexPlus to send me the equipment and figured I'd use it with my girlfriend—until I realized that was the dumbest idea I'd ever had. Thinking more clearly, I decided this might be my one chance to get a porn star to have sex with me.

Wicked Pictures, a major adult-entertainment company, set me up on a cyberdate with one of its actresses, Alexa Rae, star of *Porn-o-matic 2000* and *Say Aaah*. I had never seen Alexa's work, but I was assured she was a complete professional. SafeSexPlus.com sent both of us toys, and we made an e-date.

> **"** My favorite thing about the Internet is that you get to go into the private world of real creeps without having to smell them. **"**
>
> —Penn Jillett

I cannot fully describe to you the absolute repulsiveness of the sexual aid I was given—both because this is a family magazine and because the English language is not equipped for the task. It was supposed to be a disembodied part of a woman, but it was more like part of a really expensive Halloween outfit to which someone had haphazardly taped a lock of Dweezil Zappa's hair. It felt like wet latex, smelled like wet latex, and looked like something Sigmund Freud might have used to make a very twisted point. I figured it was designed for men without hands.

The device plugged into an electrical outlet and came with suction cups. This frightened me even more than the Zappa hair until the people from Safe-SexPlus explained that I was supposed to stick the suction cups on my computer monitor once the "cyberdildonics box" popped up. This box could be made darker or lighter by Alexa's controlling the box on her screen and would make my latex gizmo vibrate at higher or lower frequencies depending on how much light she decided to give me. I don't know what sexual experience was supposed to be replicated by a vibrating disembodied female body part, but I didn't want any part of it.

I was to have the same sort of control over Alexa's marital aid, which I assumed would be somewhat less terrifying.

I assumed wrong. "It's a little scary," Alexa confessed as we talked on the phone and I squinted at a live picture of her on a tiny, fuzzy box on my screen. I'm pretty sure she's pretty and possibly blond. "It looks like it might hurt me. And it's making these ramming noises. Like a jackhammer." I had never prided myself on being a gentle and considerate lover; *ramming noises* and *like a jackhammer*, however, were not phrases I was used to hearing.

Alexa, ever the playful one, told me she'd take off her top if I could make her light box change colors, so I got one of the tech guys at work to help me. Soon I could see her yawning on my monitor. This, I thought, was getting to be more like the sexual experiences I was accustomed to.

After 20 minutes, I think I got the color to change and the scary jackhammer noise to increase. "I get turned on by anything sexual," Alexa purred as she took off her top and jeans. "But not this."

We talked some more, and she told me she'd named herself after Billy Joel's daughter, which I thought was in bad taste. Then I realized, looking down at the giant latex pudendum jumping around my desk, that I wasn't in a position to comment on matters of taste.

Still, in the name of science I concentrated on the image of Alexa on the screen and tried to act sexy. "You are driving me crazy," I told her.

"Really?" she responded.

"No."

"Damn."

This was the high point of our encounter—that and when I admitted I was incapable of having phone sex. "Having good phone sex is just saying how you feel," she told me.

"I feel silly," I confessed.

"Not like that."

Eventually we decided to stop. "It has nothing to do with you," she said.

"We're just asking each other technical questions, and it takes away the sexiness." Virtual sex was indeed eerily like real sex for me.

Even if the technology vastly improves and if Alexa and I can one day consummate our awkward phone conversation, I don't think teledildonics is the next generation of pornography. Perhaps it might replace 900 numbers, but that's about it. Most people will still want to enjoy their sexual fantasies alone, because even a programmable robot is going to be just an annoying, unsuccessful intermediary—not to mention a very difficult thing to hide in an underwear drawer.

And as far as real sex goes, no high-tech device can ever replace a living, breathing person. Because even if a machine felt real and looked real, it could never reproduce the real thrill of sex: knowing that another being is freely giving herself to you and that at least for a few minutes, you're not alone.

Now, why couldn't I come up with something like that when I had Alexa on the phone?

THE FUNNY PAGE

"No doubt about it. The Internet poses a great threat to personal privacy."

HELP ONLINE

MY NAME IS NED, AND I'M A CYBER-A-HOLIC

Spending more time in cyberspace than in your workspace? Either get
a job or add this site to your favorites. It's the homepage for the
Center for Online Addiction. Log on to break free from an addiction to
cybersex, day trading, e-auctions, or online gambling. The group
offers self-help treatment and recovery literature as well as live
cybercounseling to help you kick your compulsion. Or you could
just chuck your computer out the window.

www.netaddiction.com

THE DATING GAME

Here's a game you can't lose. It works like this: Choose from a long list
of women from all over the world. Read their profiles, then pick three
bachelorettes to be the contestants of your very own dating game. Ask them
three questions, and pick a winner based on their responses. Your e-mail
address is automatically sent to the winner, and then the games *really* begin.

www.intermingle.com

CALLING ALL COWARDS

Too chicken to ask her out? Send her an anonymous e-mail through
secretadmirer.com. Include a Shakespearean sonnet or a line
from *Casablanca*. She'll find it so romantic she'll likely overlook
your cowardice. If she takes the bait, you'll get a message back from her, and
she'll receive an automatic message revealing your identity.
The service is free, so be willing to drop some cash on the first date.
You don't want her thinking you're a coward *and* a cheapskate.

www.secretadmirer.com

MAN'S GUIDE INTERVIEW

Cybersex, Hard Drives, and Videochat: There's More to Online Sex Than Meets the Eye

An Interview with Mary Madden

If cybersex, to you, means a couple of college kids on their respective sides of the Atlantic jerking off over AOL, prepare yourself for a shock (literally). Want a partner who doesn't ask you to take out the trash? You can find her online—if you don't mind spending $5,000-plus to have sex with a "woman" who looks like a corpse. Think it would be nice not to sacrifice nookie with your wife while you're at that monthly sales conference? Plug in and hook up. She'll quit nagging you about all those business trips. Simply feeling horny? Meet a "nice girl" through the software that comes standard on your PC.

One recent afternoon, we sat in the office of Mary Madden, professor of a groundbreaking new course titled "Exploring Cybersexualities" at San Francisco State University, as she explained the world of cybersexuality that extends well beyond chat rooms and online personal ads.

MAN'S GUIDE: Let's start by defining terms here. What is cybersex?

MADDEN: I define it for my class as sex that depends on computer technology. So anything from surfing porn to cyberdildonics to bodysuits . . .

MAN'S GUIDE: Bodysuits?

MADDEN: There's a company called Vivid; they make porn movies. Now Vivid Entertainment is making a cybersex suit that interacts with the DVD player. So depending on what happens in the video, you receive different stimulations from the suit. They tickle, vibrate, pinprick, heat, and so on. But it's not ready yet, because they can't make it so it won't electrocute you when you get it wet.

MAN'S GUIDE: A little problem.

MADDEN: Yeah, and it's also not very good for people wearing pacemakers.

MAN'S GUIDE: When you say bodysuits . . . ?

MADDEN: There are a lot of ideas of what a cybersex suit might look like. There's one that was created as art by some people in Germany, called CyberSM. People could talk and interact by sending shocks to each other over the network. So instead of sending vibrations, they would shock each other for S&M play.

MAN'S GUIDE: So they would press a particular button on the keyboard and it would send a shock through the unit?

MADDEN: Yeah, or click on a certain area of the screen.

MAN'S GUIDE: What else is cybersex?

MADDEN: You can get porn on wireless handheld computers, like your Palm Pilot. There's also text chat, videochat, audio chat, CD-ROMs. There's a cute little thing called a Lovegety—a little key-chain device popular in Japan. There's one for men and one for women. You can set it for whether you want to just talk, or if you want to be just friends, or if you want to have fun. So if someone else is in the same area you are and has their Lovegety set to the same setting and they're the opposite sex, you can find someone in person that way.

MAN'S GUIDE: What does it do to tell you this?

MADDEN: It beeps.

MAN'S GUIDE: And then how do you know who the person is?

MADDEN: You have to find out. I guess that's part of the fun.
    And do you know about cyberdildonics? They're just basically reg-

ular sex toys with an interface to your computer. You plug an adaptor of sorts into the sex toy and attach a connected adaptor to a special area on your computer screen with suction cups. The person at the other end controls the speed of your sex toy over the Internet.

MAN'S GUIDE: So then the other person uses the mouse to control the speed of a vibrator or vibrating sleeve . . . ?

MADDEN: Yeah, and you could do the same for them.

MAN'S GUIDE: How do you hook up with someone?

MADDEN: To use the cyberdildonics, you buy the toys, then simply log on to a Web site like ifriends.com and find an "exhibitor" from lists broken down by gender, etcetera. You have to pay for that. Or you could use the free software they provide to communicate directly to your own partner through a Web browser. That is free.

For free, live Web-cam-to-Web-cam audio-video action, you need a PC with a Web cam, a microphone, and NetMeeting software installed. Then you visit a site known as an Internet Locator Service, where you see a list of people's handles and a very brief headline-style description of what they are looking for. You can talk to people from around the world. They are mostly looking for someone else to masturbate in front of and someone to watch them masturbate.

MAN'S GUIDE: So it's just like any kind of chat situation in a way.

MADDEN: Yeah. I guess Microsoft meant for their software to be used for business meetings at a distance, and that didn't really work out. It's very popular software now.

I should also mention peer-to-peer porn. Instead of going to a Web site and saying, "Oh, here's a porn site and I'm going to look at the porn here," people will create networks for sharing pornography. It's like a porn Napster.

Also, do you know Realdolls? You've got to see this. [She logs on to www.realdoll.com.] This is basically a sex doll—which Howard Stern talks about all the time—that I guess looks and feels fairly realistic. You can order different models. They're all life-size and come with a little outfit and stuff. Anyway, they're working on a Realdoll robot—a doll that will blink randomly, respond verbally when touched erotically. She'll greet her man and even contract genitally during sex.

MAN'S GUIDE: Is there a male version?

MADDEN: For a while they said they couldn't get the doll to go from flaccid to erect. But they do offer a male version now.

MAN'S GUIDE: Pretty soon, we're not going to need to interact with actual human beings.

MADDEN: Well, I don't know. It would be kind of boring. You miss out on all the quirks, the spontaneity. And a doll is not going to love you.

Force feedback is another technology that's emerging, and this technology will let you feel what you see on the Web, so instead of just looking at porn on the Web, you'll be able to feel it.

MAN'S GUIDE: And how would that work?

MADDEN: People are creating different interfaces for it. There are currently joysticks and mice, but people are working on other forms too. It could also be incorporated into a cybersex suit. Also, sensors are being incorporated into computers and implants. There's a professor in England, Kevin Warwick, who has an implant already; and his wife is planning to have an implant, too, to experience sex from the other person's perspective.

MAN'S GUIDE: So, why teach a course on cybersexuality?

MADDEN: The main goals of the class are to distinguish the cybersex hype from the reality, to explore the variety of cybersexual experiences that do exist, to envision what might exist in the future and how the creators of our digitally mediated future might shape cybersex in a responsible way. The students envision their own cybersex systems and share their ideas with the class. We also look at the news media's coverage of cybersex, government involvement and censorship, and how people are making money with cybersex. The people who create cybersex interfaces will shape the future of sex. And right now, those people are online pornographers. And a few artists.

MAN'S GUIDE: How are they going to shape the future of sex?

MADDEN: In a lot of ways. When we have cybersex, we're using typed words, or voice, or video, but the bodies aren't together. At the same time, reproduction is leaving the body, with the creation of the artificial womb. So sex and reproduction are leaving the body.

MAN'S GUIDE: In your course description, you talk about how sex and technology are developing together. Can you elaborate?

MADDEN: For a long time, people have been imagining new technologies for cybersex, and now they are beginning to become realities— like force feedback, an integral component of a satisfying virtual-reality sex experience.

Another thing that's becoming more popular in computing is wearables. The wearable computer will monitor your physiology and become a part of you, a part of your life. So, for instance, if you were to stare at a person for a certain amount of time, your wearable would exchange your business card with them. It's watching your eyes, where your glance is falling and how long it's there. It's monitoring you. A professor at the MIT Media Lab created this technology. Something like this could also be applied to love and romance. Let's say you see someone new and, for instance, you have been staring for a while, and your

perfect figures

BECAUSE IN CYBERSPACE, NO ONE REALLY KNOWS WHAT ANYONE LOOKS LIKE.

Percentage of Internet users surveyed who report that their cybersex encounters have led to real-life encounters: 31

BECAUSE PEOPLE YOU MEET ONLINE ALL TURN OUT TO BE 400-POUND TRUCKERS NAMED LLOYD.

Percentage of these encounters that lead to permanent relationships: 5

• • • • • • • • •

heart rate shows that you may have romantic feelings for this person. Your wearable could prompt you to go talk to the person, send a flirtatious message, or maybe send your contact information.

MAN'S GUIDE: We're assuming all this stuff we've been talking about costs money? Clearly those dolls cost money, but that 'Net-meeting scenario you were talking about . . . ?

MADDEN: You need a Web cam. But the software comes free on your computer.

MAN'S GUIDE: What else is free?

MADDEN: If you're industrious, you can find almost anything for free.

MAN'S GUIDE: Downloading porn generally is not free, though.

MADDEN: Generally not, but you can find it for free. And when people are doing peer-to-peer porn trading, that's free, until the porn industry makes like the record industry and clamps down on it. I think that with every new technology, porn will be free at least for a while.

MAN'S GUIDE: Given all the failed dot-coms, as opposed to the continuing success of the Internet porn industry, do you think that in 5 to 10 years the Internet will be all porn, all the time?

MADDEN: I don't think so. It's kind of a saturated market. And the big players are going to become bigger. Only people with a lot of money are going to be able to deliver porn video over the Internet—and there are people with a lot of porn already made, so it will be cheaper for them. Someone like Vivid Entertainment, they'll probably be one of the big players—people who already have the money, the reputation, and the content. How are the little picture sites going to compete with that?

MAN'S GUIDE: So you think small sites will be put out of business, just like Amazon shut down all those small bookstores?

MADDEN: A lot of them already have been. And people who thought they could make a ton of money by starting up their own live-sex Web cams, they've learned that it's not the golden goose it was.

MAN'S GUIDE: What do you think it says about us as a society that porn sites appear to be the most frequently visited sites on the Web?

MADDEN: I think it's just human nature to be interested in sex. And with every new communication medium, people are going to try to communicate about sex. That was never quite so easy to do—with privacy—before. You had to go to the bookstore and buy a magazine or whatever; it's kind of embarrassing.

Now, you don't have to be embarrassed: You just sit at your computer and look at whatever you want. I think part of the reason it's so exciting to people is that it's forbidden—or it was, anyway. And when there's a crackdown on it, it's going to become even more exciting to people.

MAN'S GUIDE: And you predict a crackdown based on . . . ?

MADDEN: Well, maybe with George W. Bush as president. I wouldn't rule it out.

MAN'S GUIDE: What does a guy need to know about privacy on the Internet? Who's watching him?

MADDEN: You're probably not doing anything in private any more. Just forget about it.

MAN'S GUIDE: Even at home?

MADDEN: Maybe once you were; but now, probably not.

MAN'S GUIDE: So marketing firms are watching?

MADDEN: The site you visit could leave cookies on your computer. Also, every image you download, there's a cache of it on your computer, so companies can look at it and see what clicks you've made along your path.

MAN'S GUIDE: Like the proverbial Big Brother.

MADDEN: Oh yeah. There's nothing private anymore.

MAN'S GUIDE: That's disturbing. If the computer makers were smart, they'd lobby against that.

MADDEN: Actually, some of the computer makers are building in things that let people monitor you. Intel was going to do it with the Pentium III chip. The chip allowed outside parties to track a user via a serial number, without the user's knowledge. If you wanted to surf privately, you would have to open up your computer and switch the chip off. Privacy groups demanded that the FTC [Federal Trade Commission] prevent shipment of the chip. People called for a boycott. Intel ended up shipping the chip with the tracking feature turned off.

MAN'S GUIDE: What was the thinking there?

MADDEN: Intel claimed it was to protect users from fraud. But privacy groups believed it was a way for Web sites to collect information on a user's online activities to create individual marketing profiles. A lot of people want to find out your habits so they can sell you things. Let's say you have a porn habit, and you visit a lot of sites featuring Asian breasts. The folks that have access to your individual marketing profile will know that you have an Asian-breast fetish, and they will aim their Asian-breast-site advertising at you.

MAN'S GUIDE: Our computers know us so well.

MADDEN: It's the same thing when Amazon recommends books to you.

MAN'S GUIDE: Moving on to a less disturbing area: How can men use the Internet safely to enhance their sex lives?

MADDEN: It depends on: Do they have a partner? What are they looking for? Basically, whatever appeals to them, they can find it online. Whatever their fantasies are, they can find other people who are interested in the same thing and find sites that are interesting to them. And they can form communities of people who are interested in the same thing.

MAN'S GUIDE: Can couples really use the Internet to enhance their sex life together?

MADDEN: Well, sometimes couples go online together. And sometimes they're looking for another couple to play with, or one female or one male. Or they're pretending to be one person, or one of them is pretending that she's the male and he's the female. Or they can take on different identities. Some people have sex with each other in front of the camera.

MAN'S GUIDE: That makes us think about fidelity issues. Some consider it cheating when one partner engages in cybersex unbeknownst to the other. What do you think?

MADDEN: Some people think that it's not—it's like the Clinton theory: "I didn't have sex with her; she had sex with me." Or that it's not sex because it's not penetration. Some people think that since there's no actual person right there, then they didn't do anything. I think it's whatever the couple decides.

MAN'S GUIDE: Do you have any advice about how to detect cyberfibbing—chatters who misrepresent their age, gender, or other aspects of their identities?

MADDEN: I think that since there's no real way to tell, you have to kind of accept that. But part of this whole thing is that people are expressing different parts of their sexuality and different parts of their personality in whatever way they can. It's not really accepted in this culture for a man to walk around in women's clothing. Well, on the Internet he can find acceptance because . . .

MAN'S GUIDE: Nobody knows.

> **MADDEN:** Right. So I think part of the reason people are doing that is because of the repressive nature of our society. The Internet allows people to express themselves.

MAN'S GUIDE: What about the issue of harassment and cyberstalking?

> **MADDEN:** Online relationships—especially text-based ones, I think—seem to go hand in hand with obsession. This is partly because the relationship is not conducted in "real" space but in the imagination. You spend a lot of time thinking about your partner, anticipating their e-mails, or looking forward to meeting them in a chat room. It can actually become quite intense. Also, it has something to do with the participants. Often, people who are looking for romance online are feeling somehow isolated in their real lives. They are having trouble finding a partner, or they are feeling estranged from a partner, and they feel a need for attention and intimacy. These things add to the possibility for obsessiveness. It can be very difficult to end an intense chatting relationship. Some of the participants are obsessive types. So you have to be more careful about what you reveal.

MAN'S GUIDE: Do you think the medium gives people license to say and do things that they wouldn't normally do in person?

> **MADDEN:** I think it does. The perceived anonymity makes you feel more free.

MAN'S GUIDE: There aren't many laws yet relating to cyberstalking and harassment, so ostensibly a guy could get away with a lot. Are there any definitions out there?

> **MADDEN:** Of cyberstalking? The Department of Justice defines it as "using the Internet, e-mail, or other electronic communications devices to harass or threaten another person."

MAN'S GUIDE: How can parents protect their kids from (a) child predators and (b) stumbling onto sex sites?

MADDEN: There is one way for parents to protect their children on-line: They *must* supervise them. Studies have shown that most parents supervise their young children's online activities only moderately. And when [kids] get older, [parents] rarely supervise them at all. Most parents let their kids go online every day, and they do not restrict their time online. A surprising number of children—18 percent, according to one study—intend to meet someone in person who they have met online. Another study showed that 20 percent of kids online had been propositioned for cybersex by a stranger. Parents can use content filters, but they are unreliable, and they can't protect the kids from predators. Only parental supervision will protect them.

MAN'S GUIDE: Finally, everything we've talked about today makes one wonder: Do you think there's a difference between how people in the Internet generation relate to each other and how people from pre-Internet generations relate? For example, people didn't used to have access to live, interactive pornography the way we do now. Is that changing the way we relate to each other sexually?

MADDEN: Kids always find a way to look at pornography. I don't know how often young people without credit cards have access to interactive porn or how that might affect them. But I do think that instant messaging, e-mail, cell phones, and mobile messaging have changed the way young people form and conduct romantic relationships.

QUICKIES

ARE YOU A CYBERSEX ADDICT?

Trying to figure out if your cybersex life is a diversion or an addiction? Here are some of the 34 questions from an Internet Sex Screening Test you'll find on the Web site of Patrick Carnes, Ph.D., clinical director of sexual-disorder services at the Meadows Institute in Wickenburg, Arizona (www.sexhelp.com).

- I have some sexual sites bookmarked.

- I spend more than 5 hours per week using my computer for sexual pursuits.

- Internet sex has sometimes interfered with certain aspects of my life.

- I have participated in sexually related chats.

- I have a sexualized username or nickname that I use on the Internet.

- I have masturbated while on the Internet.

- I have accessed sexual sites from other computers besides my home.

- I have stayed up after midnight to access sexual material online.

LONG-DISTANCE RELATIONSHIP GONE BAD

A word of caution to porn surfers on the Web: You may find yourself drowning in a sea of long-distance calls. A popular scam at some "free" porn sites is to make you download software that resets your modem to dial far-off, obscure nations like, say, Chad or the Polynesian island of Niue.

Makers of these "sex dialers" sell them to adult Web sites and get a cut of the profits from routed calls. Also getting a piece of the action is the adult Web site, the network that carries the call, and the receiving country. And you, the consumer, will be hard-pressed to get your money back.

How do you avoid this? Be skeptical when a site offers so-called free material. Always read online disclosures carefully. And be suspicious if you see a dialog box on your computer indicating that it's dialing when you didn't tell it to. Cancel the connection as fast as you can, and hang up. If you do find unauthorized charges on your phone bill, contact the Federal Trade Commission at (877) 382-4357 or www.ftc.gov.

Or, you could stick to conventional porn.

CYBERBRAGGING RIGHTS

Keep your morning-after boasting to yourself. A young British lawyer learned this lesson the hard way. When Bradley Chait received an e-mail from a woman praising his prowess in bed, he forwarded it to six pals, adding, "Now that's a nice compliment from a lass, isn't it?"

Trouble was, one of those buddies forwarded the electronic mash note to other people, and before long it was being read as far away as Australia, not to mention by colleagues in Chait's law firm, whose partners may have taken him to the woodshed.

The law firm released a statement stating that it prohibits employees from sending obscene e-mail. In the end, no one was fired, but "they *were* disciplined." And according to the *Independent* newspaper of London, "The employees concerned are horrified by the consequence of their actions." Although clearly not by the juicy exploits detailed in the note.

ASK THE SEX DOC

Q: *I recently met a woman in a chat room, and we've really hit it off. We're planning to meet soon. She says she's clean, but how do I know I won't catch something from her?*
—F. Y., San Diego

A: You don't. In fact, research conducted by the Centers for Disease Control and Prevention in Atlanta shows that people who look for sex partners over the Internet have a much higher risk of contracting a sexually transmitted disease than do those who meet in person.

The study, published in the *Journal of the American Medical Association*, analyzed the behavior of 856 people who sought HIV testing at a Denver public-health clinic. Most were men in their early to mid-30s. The results showed that those who sought sex online had more exposure to HIV-positive partners, reported more previous STDs, and had up to 10 times the number of sex partners compared to offline individuals.

If you're going to hook up with folks you meet on the Internet, study author Mary McFarlane, a researcher at the CDC, urges regular testing for STDs. And no matter how willing your cyberpartner is, move your relationship offline for several dates before having sex. Once you've built trust in each other, you'll be in a better position to have an honest discussion about your histories and risks.

Q: *I spend a lot of time in chat rooms and on porn sites. My wrists are starting to get sore from all that typing. I think I might even have carpal tunnel syndrome. What can I do?*
—R. P., Pittsburgh

A: Get a life.

Seriously, while carpal tunnel syndrome (CTS), a painful condition caused by nerve damage in the wrist, seems to get all the attention, the most common injuries associated with typing are simple overuse injuries caused by poor form. In fact, one study found that more than 65 percent of patients referred to neurologists for CTS actually suffered from a correctable overuse injury. So if you don't want to trade in that Pentium processor for a quill and inkwell, try toning up your form.

● Get fit.

"Anybody who does data entry is essentially a small-muscle athlete and should be in shape," says hand surgeon Robert E. Markison, M.D., associate clinical professor at the University of California at San Francisco. He recommends Chinese steel balls, which you roll in the palms of your hands for a few minutes each day. (This ball handling should feel familiar to you.) We found a set called Steel Health Balls for $21.30 through http://china-shops.stores.yahoo.com.

● Stretch.

Before you start typing and at regular breaks every 20 minutes, take a minute to loosen your shoulders with simple arm circles. Stretch your wrists by extending your arms in front of you, elbows straight and palms down. Slowly bend your wrists back as far as they can go, then forward. Repeat with your palms facing up.

● Sit straight.

"Many of the wrist problems I see are a result of poor posture that tightens upper-body muscles and chokes off the vessels and nerves that feed the hand and wrist," says Dr. Markison. Adjust your workspace so you sit with both feet flat on the floor, back straight, and elbows bent roughly 75 degrees.

● Pad your paws.

If you get a pins-and-needles feeling in your hands after prolonged keyboard work, you may be pinching nerves as you're resting your hands. One solution: a padded glove called the softFLEX ($25). Call (800) 216-8415 or log on to www.softflex.com for more information or to order.

● Stay warm.

If your hands are always cold, your wrist muscles could suffer unduly. Try washing them under warm water before . . . typing; or invest in a pair of loose, fingerless cotton gloves. They'll also help clean up any mess you might make while typing.

Q: *I enjoy cybersex on my computer, but after an hour or two, <u>I find I have a hard time maintaining an erection.</u> What gremlins are at work here?*
—J. W., Villa Park, Illinois

A: While most of us sensibly associate arousal with erection, long periods of very low levels of arousal—the kind you might get from an Internet chat room—can pose a problem for even the healthiest penis. "After a period of time at low arousal (typically shorter the older you are), you enter a phase of sexual exhaustion in which it becomes very difficult to sustain an erection," says Andrew Stanway, M.D., author of *The Joy of Sexual Fantasy*. While this sexual exhaustion may not interfere with orgasm or ejaculation, it can be quite a downer as far as your erection is concerned. And men are not alone on this. After too much low-level arousal, women continue to lubricate but slowly lose the ability to climax.

The solution: Know your limits. Figure out how much time you have for arousal, and then bring yourself to orgasm before that time is up.

The Sex Doc is a fictional character.
The actual advice was provided by a variety of
medical doctors and other qualified experts.

---

credits

index

Underscored references indicate boxed text.

●D